D1453200

LEGENDS OF P. E. I.

BY

F. H. MacARTHUR

FIRST PRINTING MAY 1966
NINTH PRINTING MARCH 1988

DEDICATION

To our forebearers the pioneers of this Island, who, during the long winter nights of yesteryear, helped entertain each other by narrating such sagas as appear in this unpretentious little volume.

Long isolated from their fellow countrymen by the Strait of Northumberland, the inhabitants of Prince Edward Island developed personal characteristics and a way of life peculiarly their own.

These stories depict Islanders and their mode of life before modern transportation linked the Island Province with the mainland.

The book contains a total of fifty-nine stories set against the background of the Garden of the Gulf before the turn of the century. Some of the legends are written in the Island dialect. Many persons and places in the areas are actually mentioned by name.

The author wishers to express his appreciation to all those who helped make the publication a reality.

Legends of Prince Edward Island are the result of years spent in collecting the now almost forgotten folk lore of pioneer days.

So let the unprejudiced judge for themselves whether I have wasted my time or that of my readers.

F. H. M.

CONTENTS

CONTENTS

Minegoo was Made in Heaven

The following Indian legend informs us that, when the Great Spirit had completed his task of creation, there remained a sizable portion of dark red earth.

"This clay," he observed, "is the same color as my beloved people and I will shape it into crescent form and it shall be the fairest of all earthly places.

Thus the Great Spirit made a beautiful, bewitching island which he named Minegoo.

First, he considered placing the Island among the stars to be reserved solely for his own habitat. But upon further meditation he decided to place Minegoo in the heart of the laughing water, now known as the Gulf of St. Lawrence.

So one beautiful June morning in the dim past, the Indian deity lifted Minegoo upon his broad shoulders, flew countless miles through space, till he came to the Gulf Stream, where he gently set his masterpiece, to become the gem of the Northern Seas. Then the Great Spirit flew over and around it, and the more he gazed on Minegoo's fair bosom the greater became his joy.

The soft whispering voices of forest and winds, as they gambolled across the island's million acres, was the sweetest music the Great Spirit had ever heard; and the voice of the Gulf Stream laving its peaceful shores filled the Indian God with unspeakable pleasure, so that in the end he fell into a deep sleep, in which he beheld a thousand wonders that not even he could comprehend.

The centuries passed. Yet no mortal had ever trod the sacred soil of Minegoo. Each summer the Island smiled like a happy bride. The forests echoed and re-echoed to the songs of countless birds, and the dancing brooks and rills, sang in glee as they hurried along to join the brimming river. And in winter the Great Spirit covered his master-piece with great mounds of white ermine to protect it through the long, cold season.

Only in summer did the Great Spirit remain for long in his earthly paradise, which he loved best when the south wind, laughing and blowing, swept over it from the laughing Gulf waters. Only in summer could he stretch his form on the warm sands of the seashore and listen to the magic of it all, secure in the knowledge that here indeed was a place where one's cares vanished like mist before the sun.

Came a day when the mighty one said to himself. "Why should I reserve this beautiful place for my own selfish interest? Why indeed?"

I will give minegoo the fair, the beautiful, to my people that they may enjoy it as a happy hunting ground during the summer seasons.

And the great spirit was as good as his word. Soon the first canoes could be seen crossing the strait followed later by many others, all filled with warriors eager to see the Island par excellent, the land of glory. A few years later the Island became the summer camping ground for thousands of red men.

Many Indians still believe this pretty legend, still believe that the Great Spirit pays frequent visits to Minegoo, the Island resting on the waves.

Wigwam of Scalps

This saga takes the reader back to the year 1758, when Prince Edward Island was surrendered to Great Britain by the French after the capitulation of Fort Louisburg.

Admiral Boscawen, in his report to the Home Government, states the Island of St. John, (P.E.I.), "had been a place of hiding for the French inhabitants from Nova Scotians; and from the Island sprang the inhuman practice of killing the English settlers of Nova Scotia for the purpose of toting their scalps to the French who paid good money for them."

The claim was further substantiated by the finding of a few scalps in the French governor's home after Lord Rollo had taken possession of the dwelling.

But another historian of the period, John Stewart, changed the words "a few scalps" to read a "considerable number of scalps." While a Mr. MacGregor put things this way: "To the eternal disgrace of the French governor Villejoin, a vast number of English scalps were found hanging to hooks in his home."

(Leave it to historians to distort the facts.)

Sir Andrew MacPhail, writing at a later date, declared these accusations against the French governor were utterly false.

Judging by Villejoin's letters to his superiors, one can't help coming to the conclusion that he was not only a generous person but a very humane one as well.

"It is unbelievable", wrote Sir Andrew MacPhail "that Mr. Villejoin was either a scalp hunter or a scalp buyer".

The real villain was a half-breed who made his headquarters with the Micmacs. It was he who encouraged the savage redmen in the inhuman practice. It was he who paid them good money for every English swine's scalp they brought to his wigwam. Indeed this man's hatred of the English was so bitter that he built a wigwam made up mostly of human scalps, neatly sewn together and stretched over a frame made of birch saplings.

The scalp wigwam was not discovered until 1760, when a party of English soldiers came upon it deep in the heart of the forest.

The half breed was at home, so the soldiers shot him on the spot, and then put the wigwam of evil memories to the flames.

The dying man confessed to his crimes. He said there were over 100 scalps in the wigwam, every one of them taken from the heads of English swine.

Apagwina

Centuries ago there lived on the Isle of Abegweit an Indian maiden so beautiful that the angels came to earth just to drink in her beauty.

This lovely maiden was the daughter of Chief Sarkwood and his pretty wife, Wampona.

Princes Apagwina was their only child. Before her birth, both her parents dreamed a strange dream the same night, namely, that to them would be born a daughter fairer than the fairest flower in Abegweit, and that mighty and renowned chiefs from near and far would seek her hand in marriage. And furthermore, they heard the voice of the Great Spirit himself, saying: "Name the maiden Apagwina, meaning the perfect one.

The following night the couple had anther strange dream which no one in the Island could interpret. So Chief Sarkwood, sought the advise of Chief Morning Star, who lived beyond the laughing waters of the Gulf Stream, and who was credited with being the Solomon of the Micmac tribe.

The old chief who had seen the snows of a hundred winters, listened to the words of Sarkwood and then spoke these words of wisdom:

" 'Tis a good omen this dream, brother. This unborn child you sired will be the fairest of all the Great Spirit's creations. When she reaches maturity, her hair will reach down to the rich red soil, and her eyes will shine like dew drops in the heart of a lily; her face shall be like the eastern sky on a June morning. The women who look upon her exceeding beauty will be burned up with jealousy. Many Redmen will want her to wife, but Apagwina must never marry."

"Is that all the dream says?" questioned the excited father. "Oh, please tell me more."

"When Apagwina reaches the age of 16" continued Chief Morning Star, "the great Spirit will come to Abegweit and bear your daughter to the stars. Never again will she return to the Island." Thus spoke the sage, the wise one.

Then they parted company. When Sarkwood returned to the Island and to his own wigwam, Wampona had already given birth to her baby and there was great rejoicing throughout the land of Abegweit.

This remarkable child (so we are told) could walk and talk right from the day she was born.

The years passed, and Chief Morning Star had joined his forefathers in the Happy Hunting grounds. Apagwina was now 16 years of age and, as foretold by the dead chief the Great Spirit came and took her away to dwell with him among the clouds.

Sadly Wampona and the chief watched the pair sail through space on great silver colored wings. Higher and higher they rose till, finally, they were lost in unlimitable space.

But that night, when the inhabitants of the Island looked toward the Western horizon, they saw a new star, larger and more beautiful than the other stars and they were happy.

The Clanking Chain

Tradition says old drunken Bill McGee was born in the shadow of a church near Bedeque. His conscience, though seared by sin and liquor, still functioned. Like a lot of other drunks, Bill took the pledge every six months, and confessed his sins to the parish priest at the same time.

If Bill were alive today he'd be called an alcoholic — in those days they were drunkards, or as one old lady put it, "rumhounds".

Liquor and its attendant miseries were but a part of McGee's colorful life.

When John Barleycorn thought it was time to take his pal on another binge, he took him away from his farm and family to a wayside inn some half mile distant.

All children and all dogs loved Bill. They took to him like a bee takes to honey. His own dog, Major, worshipped the very ground under his master's feet.

One night while walking home from the tavern — he was well in his cups — he decided to take a short cut through the graveyard — something Bill would never have done had he been sober. However, inspired by John Barleycorn, he went on, casting only sidelong glances at the tombstones; and trying to reason with his clouded brain just how it would feel to be lying under one of the stones with a lot of earth piled over you.

The loud rattling of a chain brought Bill out of his reveries in quick order. He stopped, listened, made a few steps, then stopped and listened carefully again.

Yes, it was the rattling of a chain all right, and as he stood there the sound grew louder and nearer.

He started to run, but something held him back. He couldn't see anybody, yet he felt the grip of a hand on his coat tail. Vainly he tried to pull himself away. That's when the cold shivers started running up and down his spine, and his breath came in labored gasps. Poor old Bill! Never was a guy in a worse dilema!

How long McGee was detained in the cemetery he never knew. Certainly it was quite a while for when the thing finally released him it was breaking day.

He had not traveled far, however, when the clanking chain reached his ears again, while from out of the forest bounded Major, his tongue hanging out and his sides moving rapidly like a worked bellows, while from his neck dangled a length of chain.

Old Bill never could figure out how his experience in the cemetery got nosed about. Certainly, Major never told it, and there was nobody else beside himself in the place of the dead. It was a mystery.

When his friends kidded him about the affair, Bill would argue that the small piece of chain attached to Major's collar couldn't possibly have made all that noise. Anyway, Bill never touched a drop of liquor again.

A Cape Wolfe Tale

At Cape Wolfe in days gone by, lived John French and his mistress, Janet Daisy. Tradition says these two lived at the cove when Gen. James Wolfe set foot upon this part of Prince Edward Island in 1759.

The place had no name in those days; and only a few distant neighbors shared the lonely, wind swept place with John and Daisy. But a group of fairy folk dwelt in an old tumbled-down house some half mile up the coast.

It has been said that twice every year on May Eves and Hallowe'en, the little people made the very rafters of the old house ring with pretty dances, heavenly music, and catchy tunes.

Incidentally, this abode was known far and wide as "The House of Death" on account of its once having being the scene of a terrible tragedy. The family who occupied it died one by one of some mysterious disease.

The few settlers who lived in the district had a great fear of the place, not because it was now the abode of the little people, but rather because of its melancholy past.

During the fairy holidays revels took place within the House of Death and passers-by claimed they observed little figures flitting to and fro as they went about their various tasks.

John boasted he'd seen the little people from a distance, heard their laughter and the patter of their tiny feet, as they tripped the light fantastic to the music of flute and fiddle, but that he'd never entered the house itself. However, John believed in the little people and often told Janet he'd like to join them. So one Hallowe'en night after the pair had quarreled bitterly, John put on his cap and coat and made straight for the fairy abode, despite all that Janet could do to persuade him how foolish he was acting.

The place was aglow with lights of many colors; but what surprised him most was the appearance of the dwelling which looked almost new under the light of a full moon. When he stopped momentarily to take in the scene the elfin revelry got under way in real style, and the noise of laughter, music and dancing filled his ears and made him all the more determined to proceed.

About a score of little people were dancing to the music of flutes and fiddles, while others stood about talking and drinking nectar from tiny silver mugs, no larger than thimbles.

"Welcome, John!" they chorused as soon as he'd entered the room. "Welcome to our little party!"

John joined in the merriment and was

having such a gala time that he forgot all about Janet, for the time being.

Finally the party broke up. The lights went out all over the place and every single one of the little people having vanished as though the earth had swallowed them up, poor John found himself standing beside a ruined old house, shivering in the cold night air.

Where've you been all night? questioned Janet when he finally reached home. "And what in the world have they done to you? Why I declar you are no bigger than a midget."

But when Janet was told about the night's adventure John had in the famous house, all she could manage to say was! "Well, now, bless us and save us! Think of it!"

John took a good look at himself in the mirror and was not at all surprised to observe that he had become a very tiny person, thanks to the magic of the fairy folk. Now was he unhappy about the change, for deep down in his heart he greatly admired the little people and had entertained the hope that one day he would become one of them.

Tradition tells us that after these startling events, Janet returned to her own folk, while John went to live with the fairies, that he married a little cutie and that, eventually, they became king and queen of all the island's little people.

Paddy Dougan's Wife

Paddy Dougan's wife, Bridget, had one of those ailments which nobody, not even the best medicos could understand.

She was sick one day and she was well the next. She was as some ladies wish to be who require a lot of attention, in a state of health between being sick and well. She claimed to have a knawing feeling about her stomach every time her husband had set his mind on going to see a hockey game or down to the tavern for a glass of beer, yet if the gossiping kind of neighbors she liked dropped in, Bridget would laugh and gossip with the best of them all evening.

The poor soul was delicate beyond belief, and had no appetite for anything but the best food and drink. Poor Paddy always was led to believe that his wife needed a lot of special loving and the best of everything which he simply could not afford — that is, he could not afford anything but the loving and even this was a bit more than he could take at times. There was one thing, though, that comforted her; she wouldn't be around long to bother anyone, least of all her dear husband, Paddy.

Well, as we have said, Bridget was an invalid of sorts, trying this and that medico without benefit, until Paddy had so many doctor's bills hanging from his shoulders they bowed his once manly figure and kept his nose to the grindstone until it became razor sharp.

It was now some ten years since Bridget became half well and half sick, and on this particular morning she was moaning as she rocked herself back and forth in grannie's old chair, when an old woman, wearing a red skull cap and dressed in skins, enters the home without having been announced and seated herself beside Bridget Dougan and said:

"Well, Bridget," ye'd had quite a stretch of sickness these past ten years, and you're just as fer from being cured as ever."

"Right you are," said Bridget. "I was thinking the same thing when you dropped in this minute."

"Well, it's yer own fault that yer ill," said the little old woman who refused to give her name.

"How's that?" said the patient," surely you don't think I enjoy poor health, do you?"

"Well, not exactly," said the other, "But let me tell you this truth. Namely, that you've been annoying everyone in St. Georges for the past decade. However, I happen to belong to the order of "Good People"; and as I have a soft place in my heart for half-well-half-sick persons l i k e yourself, am here for the purpose of finding out why you've been ailing all these years, and causing that poor man of yours heaps of misery."

"Now if you'll drop this pretense of being half sick and half well, and stay well, your ailment will depart from you; so will the gnawing in your heart fade away, and you'll be as well as anyone else who is well in the Island. If you choose not to follow my advice then you must certainly remain as you now are."

Having said all this, the little old woman who nobody seemed to know bade her patient goodbye and disappeared.

Bridget, who was happy to be cured on such easy terms, followed the old lady's advice to the letter; and the consequence was, that the very next day she woke up in as good health as she ever enjoyed before she and Paddy became one through marriage.

Angels and The Little People

My dictionary defines faires as tiny spirits capable of assuming various forms and of interfering in human affairs.

The Irish word for fairy is "sheehogue". But this information fails to shed much light on the little people. Some folks claim they are fallen angels, not wicked enough to be lost, nor good enough to be saved.

According to the Book of Armogh, fairies are the gods of this earth. Certainly they are the gods of Erin, and were up until comparatively recently the gods of a large section of Lot 65.

However there is some evidence to prove they are indeed fallen angels, for like angels, they have power to make themselves visible or invisible at will.

And there are those that believe the little people are wholly earthly beings who inherit form but change accordingly to their individual whims, or as others seem to see them. Examples of this very thing often occurs in our dreams.

And still, another school of thought, is this, they are human souls in the crucible—these strange wee folk.

Those persons who believe in the Little people and claim to have seen them — my own grandmother was among this group — say that the chief occupation of fairies is making love, dancing, and playing heavenly music on tiny gold harps.

I shall never forget the day I accompanied my grandmother of sainted memories to Kellow's Brook, a happy little stream, that flowed through the center of our farm.

Grandma who had a sharp eye, picked up a tiny shoe. "Look at it my dear child," she said. "It's a fairy shoe, and finding a fairy shoe is luckier than finding a horse shoe. See how the toe and heel are worn from much dancing?"

"Yes, Grandma," said I, for I believed everything she told me about the little people including the latest saga about the tiny shoe.

Finding the fairy shoe led grandma on to her favorite topic, **fairies,** so she rambled on. "Did you know that over the sea in dear old Ireland the little people celebrate three festivals each year?"

"May Eve, Midsummer Eve, and November Eve. On May Eve, they celebrate the planting of the crops; in midsummer Eve, they rejoice over the prospects of a good harvest, and occasionally end the celebration by kidnippig a small child and carrying it away to their village to be raised as one of their own offspring. Such captives, (usually girls) are later wed to the fairy "gentry".

But November Eve, or Hallowe'en, as we now call the date was, according to an old gaelic reckoning, the end of Fall and the beginning of winter. On this night, the little people actually turned themselves into strange forms, and cast spells on man and beast.

Here grandma paused for breath as she was no longer young and we had been walking rather fast. But impatient to hear more about the doings of the little people, I observed: "tell me more, grandma, tell me more."

"Fairies are always at their best on November Eve. Besides making plenty of mischief they sing loudly and well, the favorite old Irish lyrics. And why not?" continued grandma, "for it was they who wrote them in the first place, though Carlon and Moore got most of the credit.

"Sleeping on a "rath" is what makes the fairy folk so gifted."

Not knowing what a "rath" meant and caring less, I next asked:

"Do fairies die like other people or have they immortality like angels?"

"Of course, they die," said grandma." Then she informed me of the time she attended a fairy funeral and heard the mourners singing in their tiny melodious voices. It was the grandest funeral ever. The tiny hearse containing the deceased was a garland of flowers and small tree twigs, and it was drawn by four angelic-like figures."

At this point in the story, it began to rain heavily so the tale came to a sudden end.

Perhaps its just as logical to believe in fairies as it is to believe in angels. Few persons have been privileged to see either.

They Lived and Died Under

A Curse

Ronald MacDonald, the last survivor of his family, turned the key in the door of his home for the last time. As he left the place of evil memories, the sun was already up and birds were singing merrily to their mates. The month was June, the year 1800, the place Wolfe's Cove or Cape Wolfe.

Young MacDonald's heart was heavy with tragedy, as he walked down the farm lane toward the highway. Why? Well for one thing he had buried both his parents in the last month. And six months previously, death had claimed his only sister, a lovely girl of sixteen.

When young MacDonald had reached the home of his neighbor, Steve Squires, the latter was at the door to say farewell and wish the young fellow God speed.

"Are ye sorry to be leaving this place?" asked Squires, who had known the youth since he was a baby."

"Yes and no," replied MacDonald. If I knew what the future holds in store for me things might be different. Cape Wolfe is a beautiful district in which to live, and

I know I could be happy here if it were not for the curse that has followed my family ever since they immigrated to the new world — and before. I mean back in Scotland."

"Well," spoke up, Squires, "there has been a great deal of gossip going the rounds about your folk, but whether it be true or false I am not prepared to say. What I do know for certain, is that these old eyes of mine have looked upon the dead faces of six of your kin in as many years, all of them dead from some strange disease, and the doctors couldn't say what."

"Do you believe in persons and things being cursed?" asked MacDonald of his old neighbor. "And if so, what should I have to suffer for some sin some of my forefathers committed."

"Of that I cannot judge," replied Squires. "All I know is what I have seen and heard. One story I heard was that your great-grandfather murdered an innocent little girl back in Scotland, and that her father who was thought by some to be a wizard, put a curse upon your family, a curse that would remain until the last of your family died."

"What was still worse — " Here he paused, and young MacDonald requested him to keep talking. "No," said Squires, "If you've never heard all the story, then far be it from me to divulge it at this time. Anyway, such a gruesome tale would be the better out of your young ears."

"However, I'm glad you decided to leave the old place with its bitter memories. When you reach the States and get yourself a job don't forget to write. But mind, lad, if things go bad for you just let me know and I'll find a way to help you, for the sake of your dead father who once befriended me. But I have hopes of your becoming a big business man in the U.S.A., as you have a lot on the ball. See that you make the most of it!"

The conversation came to an end and the pair parted company, the one to continue his journey, the other to attend to his farm chores.

The next morning, the dead body of Ronald MacDonald was found lying in a clump of bushes beside the road. He had died without a struggle. No marks of violence appeared on his person. Was he another victim of the curse? Well, reader, you take it from here.

Were Indians The First People
To Set Foot on P. E. I.

Well, according to an old Indian legend, the Crescent-shaped Island of Minegoo was first inhabited by a race of very small people who called themselves "Tweedlers."

Regarding their numbers and place of origin we have no knowledge for, like the redmen who followed them, they left no written records to mark their place in the sun.

The legend goes on to inform us that, the Micmacs and the Tweedlers, became deadly enemies from the start, and fought each other for many, many moons, or until the little people were either killed off or driven from the Island in exile.

The final battle that decided the fate of the Tweedlers forever was fought at a placed called "Pretty Stream". On the night prior to the great battle, a band of the little folk raided the wigwam of an Indian chief and kidnapped his only son, a youth of some 13 summers old.

When the Indians learned of this atrocious act they held a powwow at which it was unanimously agreed that before another sun should set in the western sky, every

Tweedler must be put to death. So on the following morning, the two races faced each other near Pretty Stream, and thus began the bloodiest battle ever fought on the Island.

Night and day the fighting went on for a period of three days. No quarter was asked of either side and none was given. Women and children were slaughtered along with the warriors of both races, and finally, when the conflict had come to an end only a handful of redmen remained alive to view the bloody scene. The bodies of the slain lay all about the place. Even Pretty Stream was full of dead bodies while the water itself was dyed red. This red gradually penetrated into the soil until in time the entire Island took on a dark red color— the color it retains to this day.

Nosey and The Blind Man

All we know about a chap nicknamed **Nosey** is that he lived in Kings County and minded everyone's business but his own.

The more he meddled in other people's affairs the larger grew his nose so that in time it actually bowed down his head.

People were shy of meeting the fellow and, he in turn grew shy of meeting his neighbors.

When his nose became a burden too heavy to carry about, he shacked up in the forest and made bark baskets which was how he made his living.

One day while engaged in making baskets, he was addressed by a little chap no larger than Tom Thumb.

"Want to get rid of that giant beak?" said the pintsized man. "Well, all you have to do is to make a public apology to those people in whose affairs you meddled so long. Having done this, you will then go to Lake Verde and wash your face in its dark blue waters. Your nose will then dropp off and you'll be rid of your burden forever — that is, unless you forget to thank the fairies three times each day for restoring you to normalcy."

So saying, the little chap turned about, clicked his tiny heels together and vanished into the forest.

When Nosey reached Lake Verde he was amazed to see another tiny individual tapping his way along the shore and crying out loudly. "Have mercy on me!...For I am blind!"

"What brings you to this isolated place?" asked Nosey, "Or have you come to wash away your blindness in the lake?"

"I am come," said the blind man, "to drown myself in the lake, for I am tired of living without eyes and without friends."

Then throwing his cane aside he took off coat and hat and was about to plunge into the water, when there appeared on the scene the same little fellow that had surprised Nosey in the forest and said, "Why throw your life away, my friend? Things may not be as bad as they seem. Your blindness is the result of sin, but if you will pray to be forgiven and thank the fairies three times each day for opening your eyes to the evils of this world, you will, after bathing in the lake, receive your sight."

So Nosey and the blind man walked hand in hand till they were knee deep in water. Then they stooped down and washed each other's faces. But the expected miracle did not take place. Nosey still had his over-sized beak and the blind man still was blind. So they both cried out that they'd been tricked and cheated.

"Not so," said the little fellow, who, by the way, was none other than the medicine man of the Island fairies. "Neither of you deserve to be freed from your ailments. You, nosey, forgot to thank my people three times each day and you did not apologize for your meddling. And you, Mr. Blind man, forgot to pray for forgiveness of your sins, so until both of you have learn't your lesson well, you must go on living handicapped as you now are.

At this news the two got very angry and hastened forward to seize the little man and destroy him if possible.

But their arms only closed around thin air. The fairy had vanished.

The White Trout:

A Legend of the Dunk River

Long years ago, a beautiful maiden named Mary Keeping, lived with her parents near the famous Dunk River which flows into Summerside harbor.

Mary had given her heart to Prince John Knockwood, son of Chief Eagle Knockwood, who was the leader of the Island Micmacs. Two weeks before the marriage was to have taken place, the prince was drowned while swimming in the river, near the spot now known as Scales' Pond.

Mary Keeping was heartbroken over the tragedy, as she loved the handsome young brave with a love that was truly wonderful to see.

From then on, Mary spent much of her idle time treading the banks of the old river, grieving for the one she would never see again.

The neighbors did what they could to comfort the griefstricken girl, but Mary remained sad. She disappeared one day and the story went that the fairies took her to live with them.

In course of time, a white fish was sighted in the river, and local residents were puzzled. Not one of them had ever seen a white trout before and the more superstitious thought it must be a fairy: What else could it be? Fisherfolk used great precaution when angling as they did not want to catch it, or in any way harm this amazing creature of the finny tribe.

A man in Charlottetown heard about the white trout and vowed he'd catch it, come hell or high water. A white fish was just what he wanted for his collection. So he went to the Dunk River and caught the white fish — the scoundrel!

But later, when he was frying the trout, back at his home, it gave out a loud squeal which made old Ned laugh like a loon. Everyone said old Ned had the heart of a pirate. Anyway, he decided to eat the fish even though he couldn't seem to get it cooked. Several times he turned it in the pan, but with each turning it remained as white and raw as before.

"Well, it does beat the Old Boy," he said and with that he plunged his fork into the fish's side. When it let out another piercing cry, this time, like the cry of a woman, and jumped right out of the pan onto the floor. Old Ned shut his eyes. When he opened them, he saw not a fish as he half expected to see, but a lovely maiden dressed from head to toe in pure white garments. Around her blonde hair was a band of gold, while a pair of dainty feet filled a pair of dainty sea-shell shoes. Old Ned stared at her in surprise; and while he drunk in her exquisite beauty he was somewhat saddened by the sight of blood coming from her left side.

"Look! you have wounded me, you villain," spoke the girl, and she held out her arms as if she wanted someone to lean on. "Why did you not leave me in the stream where I was delightfully cool and comfortable. Why?

At these words the scoundrel cringed and begged the lady's pardon and swore that it was all a great mistake. If only she'd forgive him he would never go fishing again — at least not in the Dunk River.

"I was only waiting for my true love," continued the lady. "If he comes while I am here, I'll turn you into a horned toad."

Old Ned begged for mercy again, naturally. Then said the lady: "Renounce your sins before it is too late, you evil man. Quick, now, take me to the river at once where I belong."

"Why bless my soul," said the old Ned, "I could never drown such a beautiful creature as you —"

Before he could finish the sentence, the lady vanished, and where she had stood was the wreathing form of the white trout. Quickly, he reached down and picked it up, and fled to the river as quickly as he could make it.

Tradition says that from that day on. Old Ned attended church regularly and went to confession as well. But not even his parish priest could persuade him to eat fish on Fridays. His stomach wouldn't take it. Finally old Ned turned hermit and they say you could hear him praying at all hours for the soul of the white trout.

The Ball of Fire

Little did Donald Ferguson and Pat O'Shea dream that the greatest adventure of their lives awaited them that day as the pair strode down the county road to their homes in Elmsdale.

The shades of night were falling fast and the sky took on the appearance of a bad storm. The moon was hidden from sight underneath a heavy cloud bank. Not a single star winked its eye at the weary travellers.

Donald and Pat were deep in conversation that touched on everything from politics to the price of farm produce. Having discussed these various subjects in their own way, and to their mutual satisfaction, they now turned to the subject of weather and taking time out to glance at the sky, wondered if she would blow out, or hand them a real punch before they could reach home.

The pair walked on in silence for some while and then casting an eye heavenward O'Shea said:

"I don't like the looks of that sky at all, and I'm mighty lucky to have you, Donald, for company. It's a dreary night, it is, and the sooner we're out of it the better."

"Bah!" exclaimed Ferguson: "Yer as timid as an old maid with her first date. It's no different from other nights as far as I can see only maybe a bit blacker."

"I wouldn't speak so lightly of the sky, if I was you," replied O'Shea. It was just such a night as this that me dear old grandma got caught up —"

"Oh, park that old wives' tale," said Ferguson. "Besides, I've heard ye tell it at least a couple of hundred times." In these days, people were forever seeing fairies, ghosts, goblins, and what have you. "I've been around these parts for half a century and divil the thing I've ever seen worse than yerself, Pat O'Shea..."

The end of the sentence died on the speaker's lips, for in the twinkling of an eye a great round ball of fire descended from the sky, lighting up the countryside as bright as a June morning.

The celestial visitor came right at O'Shea and Ferguson. Quickly they stepped aside only to see it right above their heads. They described the heat from it as being v e r y powerful, partly singeing their beards.

Fearfully, the pair dodged this way and that; but it was no use. They just couldn't get away from that ball of fire no how.

Then, as if some magician had waved a magic wand, the ball of fire changed into a large ring of light. Horror of horrors! The pair found themselves within the circle of

41

fire, and from this predicament there seemed to be no means of escape. "Have courage!" yelled O'Shea to his companion. "Keep your chin up!" But the courage had by this time gone clean out of Ferguson and he moaned loudly: "Why, oh why, has this evil befallen us? Pat looked at Ferguson, and to his amazement saw the other grinning from ear to ear — and dancing wildly like an African fire eater. Ferguson's non too robust constitution had cracked under the terrible ordeal. The man was raving mad.

O'Shea tried to pull himself together. Maybe his own mind would become confused and cease to function. The whole picture was too fantastic for words. Had the universe suddenly gone haywire?

While pondering these thoughts, the circle of fire closed upon the men, tossed them into the gutter, then it shot heavenward leaving behind a thin comet like tail as it disappeared from view.

The pair reached their homes early next morning where they narrated the above yarn to anybody who would hear the story. Some believed the tale, others did not. Some maintained the fellows were drunk as owls, and just imagined the weird story.

"It's not true," said Pat and Donald. "All we had to drink last night was a bottle of rum between us and that, incidentally, is only a drop in the bucket."

Haunted House in West Devon

The shack in West Devon where Silas Miller once made and mended shoes has, like its owner, long since passed away and only a cellar depression remains to mark the spot.

Even in Miller's time, the place was old, unkept, and drafty, and in winter, long fingers of frost and snow lay along the attic beams and rafters.

Since Miller lived alone in his crude shack, and so far as the neighbors were concerned he was welcome to it for rumor had it that one of its two rooms was haunted.

But Silas said he had no fear of ghosts. Said he feared the living more than he feared the dead.

Anyway, he continued to live in the house with the haunted room until the day he was taken to his last resting place, in Mother Earth.

Having no relatives alive to inherit his miserable property, and as nobody wanted to buy or rent it, considering all the strange tales they'd heard about the place, it stood wind-swept and unoccupied for s e v e r a l years.

Persons passing at night vowed they heard the old cobbler pegging away at his shoes just as he'd always done before he passed on.

Some claimed they saw the feeble glow of his candle through the shack's one dirty window, while others swore they heard foot steps and feeble cries coming from the building at different times, when they passed that way.

Whether these noises were facts or fancies, I am not prepared to say. All I know about the case is what I've heard from old timers who claimed they'd heard from their elders. Well, one day a one-legged fellow came to West Devon and upon seeing the shack, offered to buy it if the price was right.

When the settlers told peg leg that they had nothing to do with the sale or rental of the property, this odd character said in that case he'd move right in as he needed to find a place to shelter his bones when the winter struck across the land.

When they told him the place was haunted, and that he better move along and find more suitable quarters, he only laughed in their faces and said he reckoned it would suit his fancy all right.

That night three young men of the district took it upon themselves to find out whether peg leg was in earnest when he said the place would be quite suitable, ghosts or no ghosts.

Looking through the dirty window they were amazed to see the old codger sitting on the side of the bed and taking off his wooden leg, as unconcerned as if the place had been his home for years.

When he'de placed the wooden peg on the table, he opened an oil-skin parcel and drew from it pipe, tobacco, candles, and an old map, which he studied for some time.

All three watchers had their faces close to the window when they saw the ghost of Silas Miller come from the haunted room and move silently over to the bed on which peg leg was now reclining, the open map still in his hands.

The apparition hadn't the least effect on peg leg. Indeed, he hardly seemed surprised at all when the ghost held out a boney hand, and said its been a long time Bucco, a long time.

The three watchers didn't watch or wait to see or hear any more. They fled from the scene as though pursued by the devil himself.

All that fall and winter peg leg stayed in the shack with only the ghosts of Silas Miller and the haunted room for company. How he managed to exist without fuel and other necessities puzzled everyone, but exist he did and when spring tripped across the land, he left as mysteriously as he had come.

The Haunted Room

The saga of the haunted room takes the reader back to the days when the district now known as North Wiltshire had its haunted log cabin.

The family of Irish emigrants who first occupied the dwelling, soon found themselves unable to cope with the spooky noises that came from a bedroom on the first floor. When they could no longer tolerate such goings on, they deserted the place for quieter surroundings.

According to the story told by these people, only one room was haunted, the bedroom already mention. Almost every night something could be heard walking about on cat-like feet. Then came the noise of furniture as it was being moved from one position to another. When the unseen, unbidden guest started moving things about nobody could get in a wink of sleep.

Neighbors who laughed at the tale and called it superstitious nonsense, were dared by the owners to spend a night in the haunted room and see for themselves whether the story was true or false. However, only two persons had the courage to take up the challenge. Their experience is told in their own words.

"We retired at 11 p.m.; talked for a while, and then settled down for what we thought would be a good night's sleep. Then things began to happen. First the coverings were snatched from the bed by unseen hands. Next the chairs started moving across the floor by themselves, while the bed in which we were sleeping turned around several times with the speed of a top. After this experience we got up, dressed, and left the place in fast order, now thoroughly convinced that the room was indeed haunted."

Shortly after these curious events, a second family took up residence in the cabin, but they, too, were forced to desert the place. For several years the place remained unoccupied as nobody wanted anything to do with it. The owners could neither rent nor sell it because of its storied past.

But one night when a fierce snowstorm swept through North Wiltshire, a lost traveller sought refuge in the haunted house, not knowing anything about its past history.

He entered the building and was amazed to see everything left the way it had been. Not even a stick of the furniture had been taken away; and dog tired from tramping through deep snow he naturally fell into the first bed he came to — the bed in the haunted room.

Sometime during the night the stranger was awakened by a hand at his throat. Tighter and tighter became the grip, until

47

the breath was fairly choked out of him. Vainly he struggled to free himself from this evil thing only to pass out in the end.

When he came to he was as cold as death, and no wonder. All the bedclothes had been piled in one corner of the room, while his own trousers and boots were missing.

Next morning the residents of North Wiltshire saw a strange object coming down the road, wrapped in a blanket and with jute bags fastened about its feet and legs. You guessed right. It was the unfortunate fellow who'd spent the night in the haunted room. Bill was badly shaken from his recent experience. His eyes had a frightened look about them and his usual normal speech was inarticulate and thick.

Shortly afterward the place of evil memories was burned to the ground by villagers. Where old Bill wandered to no one could say. However, it was reported that he went raving mad and drowned himself in a mill pond.

Be that as it may, the fact remains that no one should sleep in a haunted house under any circumstances. For to do so is only courting danger and possible death.

They Became Mermaids

Tradition has it that a bottomless lake once existed near Lake Verde, that beside the lake, lived a wizard named Oozoo, who kept a pack of half-fish-half-wolves in its waters.

The events I now set down for my readers entertainment, took place in the early days when the Island was owned by France, or so tradition says.

Now Oozoo was greatly feared by the settlers who took pains to keep out of his way; but when he kidnapped a beautiful young French girl and forced her to live with him, the whole community was up in arms. Finally, after lengthy discussions, the people decided to kill Oozoo and recue the maiden, come hell or high water.

So, one October night, a group of some 20 men, armed with musket loaders and swords, set out for Ozoo's crude forest shack.

A loud knock on the door brought no response, so they boldly entered the place in the hope of rescuing the girl, but she was not to be seen anywhere.

Hearing strange noises coming from the lake the party went there to investigate and were horrified to see Oozoo and the girl swimming in the midst of the strange lake swimming in the midst of strange creatures of which they counted no fewer than thirty.

At sight of the armed troupe the wizard spoke to the denizens of the deep and they raised such a chorus of odd noises as to put the fear of the Lord into the would-be attackers.

At this point the lake took on a foamy froth due to the creatures threshing violently about in the water. Frightened as they were the 20 stood their ground and waited patiently for the lake to calm, when they hoped to be able to pick off Oozoo without harming the girl.

After an hour or so of watching and waiting a great silence descended over the scene; but no sound or sight of Oozoo or his prisoner could be had. Nor was there so much as a croak from the strange sea monsters.

Where could they all have gone?

A small boat was brought into service and by this means the lake was thoroughly rowed over several times without shedding any light on the mystery.

Then someone remembered the story the lake's having no bottom in its center — the bottomless lake — where an underground tunnel was said to lead out to the gulf stream.

This, then, would explain the disappearance of Oozoo, the girl, and the others.

However, none of them were ever seen in the lake again. Tradition says that two creatures, half human and half fish, were sighted many times afterwards swimming in the waters of the Northumberland Strait.

The Burial of Mark Sims

When Mark Sims shuffled off this mortal coil some four generations ago he left a wife and three small children in dire poverty. The coffin (home-made) was given a generous coat of lampblack to make it more pleasing to the eye of the mourners. A sled was used as a conveyance, the mourners and neighbors walking behind.

There was a small cemetery several miles to the west, but for some reason they decided to bury the remains twelve miles to the east, at a place called Big Woods, Prince Edward Island.

The route of travel took the party to where a primitive tavern welcomed all passers. Here the procession halted; and, as the day was extremely cold, all except the corpse decided that a good bracer was just what they needed.

Not long after the party had entered the inn, a storm of great violence broke out so that all decided to remain for the night. The horse was led to the shelter of a barn, and the casket was taken into the inn and laid on a couple of barrels that rested near the door.

The place was dark and dreary, and to put a little cheer into the scene the flowing bowl was passed around time and again.

What! Would a little cheerfulness do any harm?

Well, they didn't think it could give offense to their dead neighbor. And if he were alive he certainly would be a man among them.

After a time conversation gave way to songs, every man of them giving a hearty lift with the chorus. The storm without might blow its worst, the mourners cared not a whit for wind or weather. Even the remains of Mark Sims were for the time forgotten.

Suddenly one of the company piped out; "Let's have a dance!"

At these words everyone sprang to his feet except one fellow who did the giggin.

Outside the wind gamboled and moaned among the pines, and great masses of drifting snow were hurled against the windows; but inside there was joy unspeakable. Indeed, the dance seemed to increase in violence with the gathering fury of the storm. To all appearances the boys had forgotten completely the funeral, their only desire at the moment being to seize time and mirth by the forelock.

But in their reckless hilarity somebody pushed against the barrels, and the shell containing the dead crashed onto the floor, parted, and deposited the sleeping cadaver at their feet.

Instantly the pleasure ceased. They were all struck dumb with the exception of Patrick Ryan, who yelled:

Boys, O boys, take a look at Sims! Bedad, he's out for a dance."

This burst of barbarous witticism set them all to laughing. So they returned the remains to the coffin and bound it together with ropes.

Not until the following day had the storm abated enough to permit them to venture outside the inn, and now the road was next to impassable. Still, they had come to bury their neighbor, Mark Sims, and bury him they would, come what might.

Again the procession started down the road; but, finding the travelling too tough, they entered the woods, dug through the deep snow and planted the box with Sims' mortal remains where the beasts of the forest would not be likely to find it.

The following day they reached their homes no sadder nor wiser men. This true tale will give the reader a glimpse into P.E.I.'s past.

The Legend of Kellow's Hollow

Travelling west on the T.C.H. motorists must cross the bridge spanning **Kellow's** Hollow, through which flows a small stream, and where tradition says many strange and startling events took place in an earlier era.

The following legend has to do with a giant pine tree and a group of spooks that lived in the hollowed out trunk of this forest monarch.

It was here that one of the early settlers to Cornwall, met his death when he was thrown from his horse while crossing the stream.

The rider's name was Jack Connaway, one of three brothers that lived near the present East Wiltshire school, and about half a mile from the spot where he was killed.

Turning back to other days and to a night in late November, we find young Connaway mounting his steed after emerging from Noah's Ark, a tavern in the village of Cornwall. Like Tam O'Shanter, Connaway rode away in high spirits for he'd had his fill of John Barleycorn. The whole world looked good to the young rider as he headed for Kellow's Hollow.

As Jack neared the famous hollow he observed that the horse seemed uneasy and a bit frightened, so to quiet the animal, he leaned forward in the saddle to pat its neck and sooth its fears by such honeyed words as: "Easy there, old girl, there's nothing to be afraid of. Easy does it. Easy old girl."

They were half way over the bridge when a terrible, blood curling scream rent the air, causing the mare to rear up on her hind legs and Connaway to fall headlong against the bridge rail.

The only witness to the tragedy was James Kellow who happened to be in the vicinity at the time and for whom the hollow was named, being that the brook already mentioned passed through part of the Kellow farm.

Legend tells us that from that time on the spirit of Connaway haunted the spot, that it frequently was seen in the presence of other creatures from the Land of Mist, and that all of them took up residence within the great tree's hollow heart.

But the strangest event of all took place several months after Connaway's death, when one night his brother, Michael, rode the same trail and on horseback too. When they drew near the hollow Jack couldn't help getting a first hand picture of the wierd event as a full moon rode a cloudless sky.

Suddenly the horse came to a full stop, snorted, twitched its ears back and forth.

Michael looked about and then for the first time he observed the cause of the beast's behaviour. The old pine tree was lit up with lights of many sizes and colors. He rubbed his eyes and scratched his beard in amazement. Never before had he ever seen such a sight. He was well aware of the Hollow's reputation and like others in the district he entertained a certain fear of the spell it seem to cast over all who entered the place.

While he gazed at the strange sight before him, somebody or something hit the tree a powerful blow that sent all the lights showering to the ground like a fall of meteorites. For an instant there was absolute silence. Then hoof beats came to his ears followed by such endearing words as "Easy there, old girl, . . . nothing to be afraid of..."

Connaway recognized the voice of his dead brother and was about to address him when he saw the fence rails at the side of the stream rise up and change into 20 white clad figures all wearing the same crazy little skull caps.

He counted them twice to convince himself that the scene before him was not some kind of an illusion. Twenty figures there were and driving them forward was his brother's ghost also robed in white and wearing a skull cap.

The whole troupe marched across the Bridge right under Michael's nose, so to speak, and the last he saw of them was just before they disappeared within the old tree.

The old pine tree has long since passed away, along with the people who used to look upon it with awe. But Kellow's brook and the legend still runs on.

The Poisoned Wine Cup

This saga takes the reader back to the days when Charlottetown was a small place with growing pains, and has to do with a wine cup whose poisoned contents brought death to a Prince Edward Island laird and his beautiful bride of two months.

The double tragedy occurred on New Year's eve at a gay party held in the home of one of Charlottetown's leading citizens. The crime was "hushed up" because the guilty party held an important position in the Island government of that day.

To expose the murder would have brought ruin and disgrace to three persons who attended the gala affair, as they were in the room when the cup of death was drunk by the husband and his young bride. Later they observed the couple fall into a stupor, which was quickly followed by death. They were quick too to observe the smile which lit upon the face of the killer as he watched the innocent victims of his foul crime struggle vainly to try and ward off the grim reaper.

In reading this unusual story the reader must consider the times in which the crime took place, for in those days the law was far too lax. Indeed, several murders are recorded where the guilty party or parties escaped scot free. Almost every community had its tale about criminals who, after committing crimes of a serious nature fled across the border into the United States from where they could not be extradited.

The person who deliberately poisoned the laird and his lovely bride remained on the Island. As a member of the elite society of the day, he had enormous influence at all levels of society, so that there was no need of his fleeing to another country in order to save his hide.

Again, only a few persons were acquainted with the real facts of the case. But none of them even suspected the motive for the dastardly crime was jealousy, and those that knew kept a still tongue in their heads, because they were sworn to silence by the murderer himself who owned them body and soul.

Not until the last one of the few lay dying did the truth come to light. That the laird and the murderer both sought the hand of Madaline Scot.

It appears that the murdered girl came to the Island on the invitation of her uncle, a person of worth and prominence. For a while, Madaline couldn't quite make up her mind as to which of her lovers to marry; but finally she surrendered her heart to the gay and worthy young laird.

The marriage brought no apparent resentment from the man who lost, and on the night of the wedding he was among the invited guests. The following week saw the three together on different occasions and in different places.

Then came New Year's Eve. The newly weds had invited a few close friends to help them celebrate the occasion, among them the man who later poisoned them with their own wine. It was he who passed around the wine; it was he who killed the friends who trusted him. However, back of this apparent friendship, was the monster jealousy; the soul of the man became stained and shrunken and evil because he had played the game of love and had lost to another.

The Melodious Whistler

On the afternoon of July 1, 1805, Col. Joseph Frederick Vallet Desbarres, accompanied by a friend, Jack Dale — the melodious whistler arrived in Charlottetown from England. The party was welcomed by a large crowd because the colonel had been sent to the Island to take over the duties of Lieutenant-governor Fanning.

The distinguished persons were taken to Fanning's home and were welcomed there by the colonial council, which read the commission and appointment, witnessed the customary oaths of office and then delivered the great seal into the hands of the new governor.

The following week Jack Dale was guest of honor at a gala party held in beautiful and historic Victoria Park.

Towards the end of the celebration Jack Dale, or the melodious whistler as some folk called him, was asked to entertain the gathering.

Silently he walked across the grassy enclosure till he came to the shelter of the park's maples and birches. Then he stopped, bowed, look up to the sky, and began to whistle.

A hushed silence fell upon the crowd, for never before had they been thrilled by such music. The very air was filled with delicious melody until the park itself re-echoed to the merry tunes. Then something amazing happened, according to those that were present, suddenly the birds of the park blended their golden voices with the melody of the whistler; the robin, the silver-tongued goldfinch; the soft rich song of the bluebird, all poured out their hearts in glad laudation, until the slim figure of the man standing under the maples appeared to be transfigured.

When the melody ceased and the loud applause ended for a breather, the whistler once more pursed his lips and blew out one single enchanting note that set the feathered minstrels crazy for sheer joy. A great fluttering of wings could be heard as a multitude of birds left their perches among the trees to fly around the head of Jack Dale, the only person in the whole world to charm the soul of man and bird alike.

The whistler's cheeks were wet with tears as he untangled himself from the army of birds and rejoined his friends.

Exactly two months after that never-to-be-forgotten celebration, the b o d y of Jack Dale was found near the Brighton shore. Doctors said he died of a heart attack.

Perhaps the strangest part of this strange tale is this: the day Dale was buried not a single bird lifted its voice in song; and the day was so bright and calm that not even a leaf on the trees that surrounded his grave stired in their sleep.

Why?

Nobody could say, but some did offer an opinion, namely, that the birds too, were mourning the death of one whose music even they could not emulate.

The Fish Jumped Into The Boat

"We don't use bait here," said a resident of Freetwon to Bob Davis and I when we went fishing on the Dunk River years ago. "We don't monkey around with such things as hooks, lines and poles, either. We just place a light in the bow of the boat and sit tight while them speckled beauties hop right into our boat. All a feller has to do is count 'em."

I never cracked a smile. But Davis did. Then he whispered in my ear. "Islanders are the biggest liars in the world. Why any damn fool knows that fish don't jump into anybody's boat!"

The old timer went about his business while Bob and I fished and got nothing but empty stomachs and sunburned faces for our trouble.

We were about to call it a day — a damn poor day — when the same man returned and laughed at our poor luck. "If you fellers would stop fooling round with bait and hooks and all that gear, and use a light on the prow of the boat you'd ketch plenty of fish and all big ones," he said.

"Do you mean to say," Bob asked him, "that you have actually caught fish by using this method you have just described to us?"

Barney raised his eye brows in a belligerent gaze. "Don't I just tell ye so?" he said. "Why only last night 10 speckled beauties hopped right into my boat and god alone knows how many jumped over it."

"Talk on!" we said. "Well, now, don't salmon drop over water falls? Of course they does. Well trout jump into a boat in the same way.

The three of us talked a little more, and then Bob said: "What do you say to giving the idea a try out after dark?"

And by all the gods, believe it or not, the fish actually did begin to come alive and jump all around us, and in no time at all, we'd captured twenty of the biggest trout you ever looked at. Not a single one of the big fellows got away either. "Well I'll be damned!" was all Bob and I could say. Bob Davis was the correspondent for the Boston Post for many years. He had fished all over the globe; but he had to come to the famous Dunk River and hear from the lips of a local resident how to catch the slippery critters by using only a small boat and a light.

One strange thing about this method of fishing is that it is little used outside of Prince County. Tell the story in Queens County, or anywhere on the mainland, for that matter, and the ardent fisherman would throw you a bucket of water if you were drowning.

I did a brief piece on the subject some years ago and sent it to Forest and Stream with the result that I was tagged the biggest liar ever by the readers. When all this criticism of my story got nosed about a few local anglers rallied to my defense, including the fellow who'd given us the tip off in the first place.

Had I not witnessed the thing myself I should never have realized the deadly effectiveness of fishing trout with a light.

It is still practised, I am told, in some parts of the Island, but is not legal any more, which is as it should be, for our wonderful shining streams would become seriously depleted unless this unsportsmanship method of taking fish was stopped.

Phantom Ship of Sea Cow Head

One hundred and seventy-nine years ago, or in 1786, a strange saga of the sea unfolded off the Sandstone cliffs, near the site of Sea Cow Head Lighthouse.

It was midnight and a fine scotch mist blew in from the sea and spread itself over land and forest. The mournful cry of herring gulls mingled with the voice of the sea as it beat savagely against the rocky coast—it was a bad night for man or beast or ship to be out in.

Into the teeth of the s t o r m rode a sturdy little schooner under full sail. A red light shone from her port side, a green light from the opposite side; and she was headed directly toward the high rocky cliffs.

Persons who were aboard that dreadful night, caught momentary glimpses of the unknown, unnamed vessel, and vowed that she had neither captain, helmsman, nor crew. In other words, she steered a reckless drunken course, toward what appeared to be her final doom.

Breathlessly the watchers waited to hear what they feared was the inevitable crash against a shore, where other equally unfortunate ships had come to grief in the past. But there was no shipwreck this time. By some magic power of the sea gods, the vessel was completely turned about so, that now she headed out to sea and safer water. Those on shore breathed a sigh of relief, for at the time they did not know that this was indeed the phantom vessel of song and story, the ship which has been seen on numerous occasions since 1786, plowing her way up and down the Northumberland Strait.

The phantom s h i p was observed by fisher folk on both the north and south side of the Island. Sometimes she appeared as a great, gray hulk looming up in misty hours of dawn. At other times she appeared like a burning derelict on the bosom of the water. But always she managed to disappear when pursued.

If there's a legend behind the legend, this scribe cannot say. But some old timers think the phantom ship was one of Captain Kidd's pirate vessels come to life after dying at the hands of a British man-o-war. Many theories have sprung up concerning the strange schooner over the years, but not one of them throws a shred of light on the mystery.

The phantom ship, first sighted off Sea Cow Head, almost a century ago, still continues to pass up and down the strait, though her visits are less frequent than they used to be. Incidentally, this is another mystery that no Islander is able to account for.

What most Islanders do believe however

is this. Namely, that a phantom ship actually does exist, that she sails the strait at intervals of 10 - 20 years, and that she has been sighted by several reliable persons at least twice during the past couple of decades.

The Devil Took The Money

There's an old saying which reads:

"A deck of cards and a crowing hen will drive the devil out of his den", and according to the following tale, that's exactly what did happen many years ago at Elmsdale, when a poker game was going at a remote farm house.

The game had been playing some time when a dispute arose among the players over a deal. Some maintained the cards had been stacked, others that the deal was carried out properly and according to Hoyle.

When the argument was at its height, the voice of a crowing hen was heard, or was it a rooster?

"Cut the arguing," said the owner of the farm. "What you fellows heard was indeed a hen crowing. You see, the hen was given to me only yesterday, and as she is the only barnyard fowl on the premises the crowing could not have come from any other source."

Rum and cards were being mixed freely that night. John Barleycorn and the Devil, while not in the card room, were not far away.

The dispute died down, at least for the

time being, and the game went on and on. Drink after drink went down the throats of the players, while on the table could be seen a considerable amount of money. The bleary-eyed men looked sharply at each other after the deals had been made, trying if possible, to read the faces and hands of their opponents — All looked at the money with covetous. greedy eyes.

Finally, one of the players was caught cheating and all hell broke loose. Players rose from their seats, cursed long and loud and threatened to break up the game there and then. Cheating was just one of the things honest players could or would not tolerate.

The accused man now began to say a few words in his own defence. But the half finished sentence died on his lips as he slumped back into his chair. Deadly silence filled the room, as from under the table could be heard the rattling of chain, followed by belly-shaking gales of laughter. The players stiffened in their seats, t h e i r hands visibly shaking. Fear played like a shadow on their unshaven faces as they vainly fought to shake the effects of the rum from their clouded brains.

A sudden gust of wind came from no-where, snuffing the candles out. and leaving the room in semi-darkness.

Then from under the table crawled a figure that everyone recognized instantly. The crawling figure rose to a standing position, all eyes focussed upon him. The cloven hoofs, the red hood, upon his head, the two-tined fork held in great hairy hands, the long, slender tail, curled about a half-nude body; and the grinning open-mouth from which issued fire and brimstone.

Not a man among them moved so much as a muscle. No words escaped their lips, though by this time they were sober enough, and perhaps sorry for it.

Now the Devil made a face about turn, gave the frightened poker hounds a withering look, pocketed the cards along with the money and fled from the place into the gray dawn of morning.

The Sacrifice of Pontacas

Chief Eagle Eye of the Micmac Indians was a mighty man in war, but not in matters of love.

He treated his loyal wife Pontacas with growing indifference, though she, poor soul, waited on her lord hand and foot. But time had wrinkled the once fair face of Pontacas, and her husband was not slow to notice the change. Yet never did a complaining word fall from her lips. True, her countenance revealed the sorrow that lay deep within her heart but as always, she somehow managed to hide it in her usual sweetness of manner.

One day when the chief was walking alone in the forest, he happened to meet the daughter of Chief Big Nose of the Mohawk Valley Tribe. Immediately, Chief Eagle Eye fell desperately in love with the beautiful Princess Novaka, who had come to the island of Minegoo to visit relatives.

Princess Novaka was a maiden to delight the eye of any suitor, tall graceful, and as fair as a morning in June. Her beautiful eyes reminded Eagle Eye of dew drops in the heart of a lily, her skin was like the soft skin of a new-born fawn. Two braids of silkin hair hung like moss on the oak tree, right down to her waist.

Their secret wooing among the tall pines soon reached the ears of Pontacas, causing another furrow of worry to spring across

74

her brow. Night in and night out, the lovers met and, when the time came for the princess to return to her own people, the chief bade his new sweetheart adieu saying: "I will come to you, dear, when the hunter's moon shines over the Mohawk Valley. Then they embraced and parted.

Sadly, the chief returned to the warmth of his wigwam — and to Pontacas, who awaited her lord's return in silence. Chief Eagle Eye ignored the look of pain on his squaw's face, ate his meal in silence, and was soon asleep. Pontacas did not immediately join him, but sat long into the night, wondering why her husband could be so cruel as to bring another woman to share his wigwam when all through the years she had served him faithfully.

Finally, she fell into a troubled sleep in which she saw her man and the strange maiden making love in the north corner of their abode.

Time passed. The autumn arrived and the corn was ripe for plucking and Chief Eagle Eye, true to his word, set out on the long journey to the land of the Mohawks. The journey occupied many days, but at last he arrived and the welcome he received from his sweetheart and her people was cordial and sincere.

Best of all, Chief Big Nose consented to the marriage which was held in the valley where the little village of Fort Plain now stands. It was a gala affair. Dancing, singing of love songs, and flowery speeches were the order of the day.

The day came for Chief Eagle Eye and his bride to separate themselves from such good company and return to beautiful Minegoo.

When, finally, their tiny canoe reached the Island, the lovers were tired and happy.

Pontacas watched them as they walked toward the camp, arm in arm. Quickly she made up her mind to sacrifice herself, as she felt she could not endure life under the same roof with a strange and beautiful young woman stealing the show. Having thus spoken, she ran to the river, plunged in, and was soon lost to sight.

The playboy chief missed Pocantas sorely as the days passed. The sweet sound of her silvery voice no longer could be heard about the place, nor did the patter of her familiar feet come to his ears.

Too late, he discovered he'd made a great mistake. The princess had beauty, to be sure but no brains. Besides, she was given to violent fits of temper that soon spelled finis to what he thought would be the perfect life.

Quarrel followed quarrel, and then, one day, Novaka was gone. Later the chief learned she had returned to her own people, and he did not wish her back.

But it must be chalked up in his favor that Pocantas remained a loving memory all his days while Novaka was completely forgotten.

The Phantom Train

The picturesque village of Wellington is situated just twelve miles west of Summerside at the head of Grand River. Incidentally, Wellington is named for the Duke of Wellington.

At the time our story opens, the village had a grist mill, a saw mill, a couple of general stores, a small Methodist church. It also boasted a doctor and post office.

Going back to December of 1885 we find the Island sleeping under a blanket of snow.

The day of December 6th, dawned bright and the air was heavy with hoarfrost. At a place called the "Mill House", a large frame dwelling, great preparations were going forward for a wedding supper that night. The bride-to-be, was the miller's d a u g h t e r beautiful Janett Crosby; the groom, one of Charlottetown's gay young blades by the name of Hilbert Coates.

Finally the curtain of night fell over the landscape, the Mill House, and its sixty odd guests who'd assembled to help celebrate the gala event.

From the windows of the Mill House could be seen a group of young people skating on the nearby mill pond. They were participating in a contest sponsored by the village smith, who had invented the skates, made of files inserted in small pieces of wood, and fastened to the foot by straps. These skates were quite common in pioneer days and were called "woodstock".

During the height of the sport's contest, a tragedy took place. A skater dropped through the ice near the flume and was drowned.

An older brother, John, vainly sought to save him, almost losing his own life in the attempt. Indeed, had it not been for a Mrs. Davis who happened by at the time and lent the gasping John a helping hand, a double tragedy might have further marred the joy of the evening.

The body of the drowned boy was carried into the Mill House, thus making it a place of mournign rather than a gala wedding scene.

Come midnight, a train was heard in the distance, all wondered at this as the regular train had passed some hours before. Suddenly the whistle shattered the stillness of that December night, followed by the ringing of the train's bell, as the iron horse rounded a curve in the railroad, not half a mile away.

Then the light from the monster's single eye picked out the wedding guests and the mourners, as they gathered about the doors to witness the phantom train flash across the railroad bridge and disappear around a bend in the track only a hundred yards or so from the Mill House.

Watchers who carefully observed the ghost monster, vowed they'd seen a passenger walking down the aisle of the coach car. One man claimed he'd heard a dog barking while being held tightly in the arms of a lady traveller. However, be that as it may, all agreed to having seen the lighted train roar by.

Among the wedding guest was a section man, James Ferguson, of Summerside. He and a couple of pals had arrived by trolley car as far as Wellington Section; so on hearing the train, they rushed to the station to retrieve the trolley before the train struck it.

Soon the young fellows returned to say that they'd removed the trolley, stepped aside to let the train go by, but to their amazement it just melted from view before their eyes.

On enquiries at Summerside it was learned that no train was despatched that night.

Believe this story or not, all I can say is that there are a few old timers around Wellington Village who do believe it.

The Meteor and The Angel

A family named Wilson once operated a farm between Cornwall Village and East Wiltshire, or near the road leading from the old Post Road to the Kingston Road, to be more specific.

Late one summer evening John Wilson and his wife, Sarah, sat on the verandah of their house watching the day depart. Mary aged six and her sister, Ruth, aged eight, were fast asleep. The evening star had already set its watch in the sky, and as the couple watched it twinkling in the distant heavens, a second star came into view, only moments later to drop from the sky.

"It appears to be falling on our farm," observed Mr. Wilson. Sarah thought so too but offered no comment. The falling meteor appeared to be descending at a terrific speed, and gave forth showers of sparks like a red hot horse shoe under the smith's hammer.

Then it hit the earth with a loud thud and more sparks shot their beams into the air.

Satisfied that the star had indeed fallen on the back field of their farm, the Wilsons set out to investigate.

By the time they'd reached the spot the meteor had cooled off quite a bit, and was beginning to burn itself into the soil. To get a better view of the thing the Wilson's drew nearer to the spot. Now they stood close together, their arms entwined. A celestial form which appeared to come from nowhere stood beside the dying star. It was holding in its arms their little Mary. Each looked at the other, amazement written across their pale faces. What could be the meaning of this strange sight? Suddenly Sarah broke away from her husband, and with outstretched arms and a cry on her lips, ran forward to rescue her daughter.

Just as she reached the spot, the meteor sank from view and the angelic creature vanished.

When the couple had arrived home they went straight to the children's bedroom on the second floor. The fear that held their hearts unsteady now grew into real anguish, for they discovered little Mary asleep in the arms of Death. Across the child's mouth lay the family cat.

The Bloodiest Battle in Island History

The bloodiest battle ever waged on the Island took place at a spot now known as Kellow's Hollow, near the present village of Cornwall. And it was fought by the Micmac Indians vs. the Tweedlers, an army of Fairy folk, who had a campsite near the little brook that still flows through the famous spot.

Tradition does not place a date for the fight, nor do we know how many were killed in the engagement.

What we do know, however, is that the Indians completely routed the enemy. Those fortunate enough to escape at the time, later were rounded up, put aboard tiny boats, and set adrift in the Gulf Stream. Tradition says they were all lost in a great storm that followed their expulsion.

Who were the Tweedlers? What part did they play in the history of the Island? The Tweedlers, we are told, were a master race of Fairies that inhabited the Island years before any Indian had set foot upon Minegoo. But the first band of redskins who discovered the sea-girt isle fell in love with its beauty. They told others of their tribe the wonders of the land, and soon thousands of their kin flocked to the shores of Minegoo.

It was for possession of this gem of the sea that many bloody battles had been waged between the races — the one already mentioned being the last.

The above myth first claimed my attention, when, many years ago, I heard the story from the lips of the late Micmac chief, John Sark. I put the legend among my treasure-house of memories, and am only now giving it to my readers for their entertainment.

Treasure Trove

Tales of finding pirate gold along the bays and coves of P.E.I. was legion in pioneer days, and among the believers was Benton Woods who lived beside the Brudenell River.

Benton told everyone who'd listen to him the following story which he said was true:

"I was hidden behind a large tree the day that Capt. Kidd and some 20 of his pirates came ashore with a couple of large seamen chests and buried them right under me nose, so to speak."

Ben kept the news to himself because he wanted whatever was in those chests for himself; but the fates cheated him in the end. It was then he informed his neighbors about the treasure trove he almost had and then lost.

It seems (according to the legend) that Woods built himself a tidy little boat, and one night, after it had been finished, he went to lift the treasure but was prevented from doing so by the ghost of Kidd. First, Wood thought it was one of his neighbours who'd somehow come upon the covered pit by luck and was at that very moment in the act of robbing him of his loot.

However, he changed his mind when he drew nearer to the pit, or perhaps I should have stated that Kidd's ghost changed it for him. For there before his amazed gaze stood the snuffy old sea dog. He wore the uniform commonly worn by pirate skippers in those days, while at his side there dangled a lengthy cutlass, fastened to his person by a wide leather belt.

"So ye came fer me gold," said the pirate King. "And don't deny it, for I can see the look of disappointment in yer eyes even from where I stand. Well, yer too late you snivelling son of a landlubber, it's gone." Woods was so taken by this sudden turn of events that he just stood there gazing at the apparition not able to utter a single word of explanation.

With a few deft strokes of a shovel Kidd finished filling in the pit. Then with a terrible oath which I dare not repeat here, he flung the shovel to one side and vanished in the nearby bushes.

Not a living thing was in sight as Woods advanced to.the spot where the rusted shovel lay. Wood picked it up and upon turning it over, discovered that some seaman artist had painted a gold replica of the Jolly Roger on its under side.

Years later, when Woods retold t h e strange tale to a younger generation, he always brought out the old shovel to back up his story.

P. E. I. Legend Has it that a Wizard's Ring was Cursed

Hector MacLeod might have enjoyed a long and happy life in Prince Edward Island, had it not been for the accursed ring given him by an uncle who herded sheep in the Scottish Highlands.

A legend connected with the gold band, was to the effect that bad luck would follow the wearer, even to the end of the earth.

Where his uncle came by the ring nobody seemed to know. But some had it that he stole it from the finger of a wizard named Ogar, who lived in a cave, during the days of Sir Walter Scott and Robert Burns.

Anyway, the day young Hector boarded the Polly enroute to the New World, the ring was on his finger.

As the ship pulled away from the quay he waved a farewell to old Uncle Niel and then mingled with the other passengers.

Among the passengers was a beautiful lass named Jean. Because she came from the western islands of Scotland, everybody called her Jean o' the Isles. Not only was she a very bonnie person, but she proved to be a fine entertainer as well. What with

her Scottish dances and songs, she bolstered the spirits of the entire company at times
when a feeling of loneliness for the land they
had left behind stole over their hearts.

Jean and Hector had appraised each other from that very first day at sea. And ob-
servant passengers noticed, with nods and
smiles, how these two young folk were falling in love. Soon the affair came to be
known as the "romance of the Polly."

One evening while the lovers were strol-
ling the deck, Hector was seized by a violent pain in the pit of his stomach and had
to be carried to his berth. Jean sent for a
Dr. Angus MacAulay, agent of the Earl of
Selkirk.

Hector lay upon his bed in great agony
while Jean and the doctor did what they
could to alleviate his suffering. But despite
their best efforts to save his life, the young
man died two days later and his body was
committed to the sea.

The day before he died, Hector had called Jean and her father to his bedside. The
former he kissed fondly; then, taking the
ring from his finger, he put it on the other's hand, saying!

" 'Tis the wizard's ring. May it — bring
you — and — Jean the the best o' luck — in
the New — World."

The day the P o l l y reached Belfast,
P.E.I. was a day of great rejoicing for all
but Jean. Her heart was too ful of sorrow

over the death of her lover to join in the general merriment. Soon all hands w e r e busy lugging their belongings from the shore to the tiny settlement, or erecting make-shift shelters to hold their meager possessions.

Time passed. The new settlement increased its numbers and prospered. Jean's father had proved himself a hard worker. At the end of ten years he owned a hundred acres of land.

One morning, while Jean and her father were eating breakfast, the girl noticed that the curious ring was missing from his finger.

"Why, father!" she exclaimed.

"Whatever have ye done with Hector's ring?"

"Well, lass," he explained, "to tell ye the truth, I lost it yesterday while felling trees back o' the shed. The thin edge o' it was cutting into my finger every time I swung the axe; so I slipped it off and hung it on a limb."

I marked the exact limb where I hung it; and when I came to get it, it had vanished — and the loss o' it has caused me a bad night, lass, a bad night indeed."

"Now, just what do ye mean by that?" questioned Jean.

"Well, Jeannie, ye know I was never one that believed in spirits and the like. But last night the queerest-looking creature came in to my — . But hark! there is some-one calling me. Hand me that lunch bas-ket, lass — the rest o' the story will keep till supper time. Good-bye, Jeannie."

That was the last time Peter MacNab was ever seen, and the more superstitious of the settlers vowed that the loss of the curious ring had all to do with MacNab's mysterious disappearance.

Did Ghosts Toll The Bell?

The morning of October 7, 1853 will always be a memorable one in the history of Prince Edward Island. For on that day word reached Charlottetown that the mail steamer, Fairy Queen, had sunk in the Northumberland Strait carrying seven of her passengers to their deaths.

Three of these were members of St. James' Church, where legend has it, four figures were seen on the church steps, while the bell tolled at regular intervals for at least half an hour.

Capt. Cross, always an early riser, had left his home in Brighton bound for the Royal Oak stables to pick up a horse he'd recently bought in England from his father's farm in Devon.

About half way over Black Sam's Bridge he heard the bell, and, believing that some strange vessel was entering the harbor, he altered course, crossed to Pownal Street and followed it until he came in view of the water front. Only a few small craft rode at anchor, their occupants apparently asleep as the hour was only 5.30 a.m.

All the while the bell kept up its measured tolling. The captain crossed to Government House, home of Prince Edward Island's

Lieut. Governors since colonial days, where he could command a wider view of the outlying waters. Not a sail was in sight. Captain Cross decided to investigate further.

He left Government House grounds and then proceeded to retrace his steps up town. As he neared the church the music of the bells came clearer.

But what were three figures doing on the church steps? The three were dressed in robes of white. A fourth figure on the belfry was ringing the bell. The sexton of the church came. Moments later the two were joined by Rev. Dr. Snodgrass, pastor of the church. All three had heard the bell tolling, but only Nicholson, the sexton and Captain Cross saw the mysterious figures in white. They had vanished moments before the pastor's arrival.

Before entering the church, which was securely locked, the captain and Nicholson narrated their story, which Dr. Snodgrass attributed to a vivid imagination. But the ringing bell was another matter. "B e t t e r get up there," said the minister. Just as he said this, the bell tolled once more for the last time.

When the captain and the sexton had climbed the winding stair to the belfry and had returned to make their report that nothing was amiss, Dr. Snodgrass was in a quandry.

In answer to their question: "Now do you believe us pastor?" the reverend gentleman turned on his heel and walked away. It was 111 years ago since these strange events took place. To this day the white clad figures and the tolling bell still live on in legend.

Pirate's Gold

Soon after the notorious Captain Kidd had been hanged in England for committing acts of piracy on the high seas, reports began to circulate in Prince Edward Island that a vast treasure lay concealed on a spot near Marshfield.

A fellow by the name of Hasket — Jim Hasket — dreamed just where the treasure lay, and so he and his neighbor Bill Heeney went in search of it. Hasket further claimed that he talked with Kidd in his dream and that the pirate told him the treasure was hidden near the shore near Marshfield. However, it was not to be lifted without a human sacrifice.

The two agreed to meet the following night, when the buccaneer would furnish further details, but before separating Kidd drew a wrinkled, yellowed paper from his bosom and handed it to the highly excited Islander. When the notorious captain disappeared, Hasket opened the faded paper with trembling hands and read the following words:

"No words must be spoken aloud during the time the treasure is being lifted and no lights of any kind are to be employed.

At the stroke of midnight you'll see my ship off shore. You'll be able to recognize her by a large red light at the bow and the Jolly Roger at the mast. I will come ashore with a few men and together we'll complete the task."

"It always had been an unwritten law among pirates that a human sacrifice be made when a hoard was buried, and again when it was taken away.

"Obey this order, Hasket or suffer the consequences.

Signed C. W. K."

The whole plan was carried out in strict secrecy. Not a soul in Marshfield save Hasket, Heeney, and two other men, knew anything about the strange affair, and these were sworn on a blood oath to keep mum.

Just before the digging began, Heaney took cold feet and wanted to call it quits, but this kind of talk so enranged Hasket that he spoke up sharply:

"Why, you was always a fool Hasket, and your bold talk may cost you your life before the day is spent" — meaning that he would be the one sacrificed when the gold was uncovered.

One fellow aboard Kidd's ship had been instructed to give three shrill blasts on a horn when the midnight hour arrived.

A great silence fell over the treasure seekers as the zero hour approached for

Captain Kidd to show up drew near. Every one stood tense. Hasket was the most excited of them all, and when midnight had passed without Kidd showing up he became very angry and cried out in a loud voice:

"Bill Kidd I command you in the name of Beezelbub to appear and deliver the goods! There was no reply. The failure of the pirate ship to appear was a great disappointment to the waiting men; yet there was hope, and following the example of their leader, they began digging furiously in the spot where Hasket thought the fortune might lay.

When the diggers had gone down some ten feet or so, water from the nearby river began to flood the hole.

It was well after midnight when a blood-curdling yell rent the air and put the fear of the lord into the diggers.

What could it be? Where did the sound come from? None of the group waited to find out. In the wildest disorder, spades were tossed aside and the gold seekers fled for their lives.

Never again could any of them be persuaded to visit the place — no not for all the riches in christendom.

The Recluse Lawyer

When a person decides to forego the friend-ship found in human society to become a hermit there usually is a worthwhile story behind the act.

Such a person was Perry Gaudet of Souris, who left his home to live in a shack near the present village of St. Peters.

Perry Gaudet was the only offspring of a well-helled family. The boy was educated to the law, and for a time practiced his profession in Halifax. Then he returned to his native Island, a sullen, silent man, who shunned all human company.

Not even his parents could break the silent barrier between Perry and the world at large. Nor could they understand his peculiar behavior, or learn from him the cause for it.

Certainly, they were a w a r e of some dark secret in their son's heart, but what-ever it was Perry was keeping it to himself.

The local priest and the village doctor tried in vain to persuade the young fellow to lay aside his troubles whatever their na-ture, and to go back in to practice.

To their pleadings Perry replied:

"I'm through serving humanity in any capacity. Soon I shall retire from society to lead the kind of life I have chosen for the future." More information he refused to volunteer; and in time people of the district decided to let him be.

Soon after this the young lawyer packed his belongings, a few favorite books being among the lot, and moved into the crude shelter already referred to.

The years passed. The recluse became a legendary figure in Kings County. When his parents died he did not attend their funerals.

Sometimes he could be seen gadding about at night, like a wild beast prowling its domain, but mostly he remained under cover.

One winter, during a bad blizzard, a group of persons went to investigate whether he was living or dead, as no one could remember having seen him for some weeks.

They found the door to the shack securely fastened from the inside, and when they called out to the recluse and received no answer, the door was forced open.

In one corner of the miserable, drafty shack, lay the remains of the hermit, frozen as solidly as a block of ice. None could say how long he was dead, or the possible cause of death. And as there was no doctor nearer than Charlottetown, the case was closed. Thus is came about that Perry Gaudet went to his grave without benefit of a doctor.

Among the dead man's meager belongings was found some pieces of gold, a large silver watch, a curious ring with a coiled serpent mounted instead of a gem setting, a photograph of a strikingly beautiful girl and lastly, a small diary which contained among other data, the following letter.

"Dear Perry:

Where I am you cannot follow. Please do not grieve too much over my passing. The whole affair has been a terrible tragedy; but such is life and some day when the veil is lifted you'll understand why this terrible thing had to be. So until then adieu my lover.

Yours forever — Pauline."

P. S. With Gaudet died the mystery of a broken heart, a mystery hidden in a lonely unmarked grave near St. Peter's Bay.

Buried Alive

Among the first white settlers buried in Belfast cemetery was a man whom we shall call Hugh McIntyre. His real name for obvious reasons must remain a secret, so as not to embarrass any descendents of his who might be living in the Island today.

McIntyre was among the immigrants who came to the Belfast district from Scotland, in 1803, aboard the good ship Polly.

Persons who knew the man well claimed he was a real scallawag, a fellow who spent most of his time drinking in taverns when he ought to have been working to provide a living for his wife and children. And when, in his cups, big Mac was quarrelsome and over fond of fighting.

The story is told that he knocked out seven rivals single handed during a New Year's celebration held in a neighbor's home.

In those days stumping "bees" were in vogue, and when the owner of a piece of land wanted to have it cleared for cultivation, he would invite all his neighbors to a stumping bee or frolic as it was sometimes called, the owner supplying free rum of course.

When the task was finished a real country hoe-down followed, in which the old and the young took part. Usually the settlers tripped the light fantastic too till the "wee sma' hourse". These gala events were held in every district across the Island, as dancing was one of the few recreations open to the early settlers.

One night while attending a dance, MacIntyre got loaded for bears, as the saying goes, and cut in on a neighbor who was waltzing with a very pretty girl. Everyone present had the feeling that a fight was in the offing, as no man worth his salt would stand idly by while another stole his partner right out of his arms.

Fighting words were exchanged between the men, a sort of preliminary to the real battle which was to follow. MacIntyre was a powerfully built man who could throw out his dukes quicker than a monkey when he got his dander up. To face him in combat, required a lot of nerve and plenty of guts.

Soon the fight got under way in earnest, and the dancers retired to their respective seats to await the outcome.

For half an hour the fighters took and gave body bruising punches that could be heard all over the house. Neither man showed any sign of chickening. "At long last," said the crowd, "big MacIntyre has got his match". And he had. The fight might have lasted much longer had not one of the male dancers floored MacIntyre with a heavy iron poker. Carried home in an unconscious condition, he died the following day — that is, they thought he was dead, so they buried his remains in the little cemetery at Belfast.

Sometime after these events, MacIntyre's family moved to Perth, New Brunswick, and settled there, and later, when the family had purchased a plot of land in the local cemetery, they decided to have the body of their loved one dug up and buried in the new plot.

The men assigned the task found the casket in an almost perfect state of preservation. Wondering if the body of MacIntyre was as well preserved they pried up the lid of the shell and took a good look. Little did they realize the surprise that was in store for them. MacIntyre lay face down in his death cell. In either hand was clutched a fistful of his own hair. He had indeed been buried alive and had turned over in his coffin.

In pioneer days many persons had a fear of being buried alive, which may have been one of the reasons why they kept their loved ones in their homes several days before committing their bodies to Mother Earth.

The Phantom Terror

The attack by the Phantom Terror had everyone in King's County agog with excitement and fear.

At midnight October 8, 1845, Mary King, 12-year-old daughter of a John and Susie King, screamed into the night:

"I've been attacked by a something . . . Come to me father! Come quickly! Someone tried to kill me, to choke me!"

Her parents sprang into Mary's bedroom on the double. Their only child lay on her bed breathing heavily. She was in a state of hysteria though able to describe in some detail just what had taken place.

"I was dozing off to sleep," she said "when I was awakened by footsteps in my room. I rose on one elbow but could see nothing. Nothing at all thought I felt its presence in the room. Then there was silence for a brief period. The footsteps drew nearer, and I could feel the thing's breath on my face. Then it was choking the life from my body.

The parents made a thorough search of the home, but found nothing to report.

"Are you sure, dear," questioned the

mother. "Perhaps it was a nightmare you had.

The girl stuck to her story: "no, mother, I tell you something had me by the throat and was choking me! I can still feel the pain in my neck."

The parents were skeptical of the whole story, but one hour later, the child had a similar experience though she'd been moved to a different room. This time Mary was actually gasping for breath when her father entered her bedroom.

Up to the time of this happening, the community where the King's lived was law-abiding and peaceful. Nothing like this had ever happened before. But now the entire neighborhood was filled with gossip over the dreadful affair. Finally, the story got to the sheriff and he investigated the case. That night, accompanied by a lawyer from Charlottetown, they stood watch about the home, the sheriff in the bedroom first occupied by Mary when the attack took place, the lawyer in an adjoining room.

Came midnight and a cry for help rang through the house and brought everyone on deck. But it was not Mary calling this time. It was the sheriff who vowed that some creature, he knew not what, had attacked him from behind while he was apparently dozing.

This time the whole group distinctly saw a strange figure vanish through the open window. Asked to describe it, not one of those present could. But all of them agreed that it was not a human being.

Outside it was raining hard and there was much soft ground, but not a trace of a footstep could they find. Here indeed was a mystery that called for a solution, but no solution was ever found. The phantom terror had made a clear get away.

After his terrifying experience, the sheriff advised the Kings to move to another house, which they did, and the house of evil memories was put to the torch, as nobody had any desire to live in it afterward.

You have been reading the case of the Phantom Terror, as strange a case of the supernatural as ever occurred in Prince Edward Island — the case nobody could ever solve.

The Recluse of Dunk River

Let me tell you the legend of Dunk River, the famous stream that flows into Summerside harbor.

Many years ago (so the legend runs) a man named Cook — Capt. Cook — received from the British Government a tract of land then uncultivated and heavily wooded.

In the fall of 1799 Capt. Cook took passage on a small trading ship for the purpose of seeing his possession, a grant from the British government in consideration of military service rendered to the crown.

Having reached the harbor of Summerside safely, Capt. Cook, accompanied by another man, set out in a small canoe to explore the Dunk River and to see his property. The pair were delighted with the scenery that spread out before their eyes, a scene unspoiled by the hand of man.

Having arrived at a spot where the river takes a sharp turn, the men were surprised to observe a narrow footpath leading up from the shore and on into the forest itself.

Leaving his companion in charge of the canoe Capt. Cook embarked to follow the path. Soon he came in sight of a little shack or hut. The building was small, yet in fairly good condition. Capt. Cook knocked on the door. No answer, but from the inside of the dwelling came the sound of music, very sweet music it was. The Captain stood where he was and listened. Now, thought he, just who would be enjoying such a lonely abode and why.

Perhaps the whole thing was a dream, the music, the little hut — a dream such as Mirza saw long years ago when he went to the mountain to meditate and pray and saw the genie.

And while he stood there d e e p in thought, a shot rang out and punctured the quietness of the lovely October evening.

Then the door of the cabin was flung wide and a strange figure stepped across its threshold. The figure was that of an old, old man, with white hair hanging loosely about his stooping shoulders. In his hand was an instrument resembling a flute. Captain Cook had seen and met a number of odd characters in his lifetime, but never one exactly like this.

Silently, at first, Cook gazed at the man who stood before him. Then he addressed the stranger, but the other only looked surprised. No words passed his lips.

This time the Captain addressed the stranger in French and got a warm smile for his trouble. Then they began to talk, and what a strange tale came from the lips of the old man. Cook was informed that the old man had lived in the wood for nigh unto 100 years, that he'd come from France and had settled near the Dunk River 60 years earlier.

But try as he would, the captain couldn't pry further information from the old fellow.

And now that my secret hiding place has been discovered," said the hermit, "I shall soon leave the Island forever."

Having said this, the strange character entered his dwelling and slammed the door shut. Captain Cook returned to the canoe.

Later he went aboard the vessel that had carried him to the new world and sailed for Halifax, where he spent the winter.

When spring came he made another trip to see how things were shaping up back where the old man lived. But when he reached the lonely spot, he found the shack a heap of ashes. Hard by, he picked up the musician's rusted flute, and a bit further to the north of where the humble dwelling had stood, he found the badly decomposed body of the old, genie of Dunk River.

John Barleycorn Plays A Joke

This little folk lore story take us back to the days of the horse and cart and when rum was so potent that drinkers just couldn't help seeing strange sights.

The setting is the city of Charlottetown, or the Royal Oak stables, to be more specific.

Tom and Jerry could be seen hitching their steed to the two-wheeled cart to begin their tiresome journey to Milton.

Both men sat on the front of their cart, their feet resting on the thills, the way all people sat who drove in carts.

Between them was a 2-gallon jar of rum, the best that money could purchase. Overhead a big moon rode a cloudless sky; and it was full, just like Tom and Jerry.

The oldtimers were as happy as Tam O'Shanter was when he rode past Galloway's haunted house. Each was smoking a corncob pipe — that is, they smoked between drinks. While the old cart rattled its way over the rough stoney country road. The beast hit its own pace. What need was there to hurry anyway?

With the jar of nectar close at hand, neither man cared a tinker's dam about time or destination. For the moment, at least, they were happy. What might take place when they arrived home and found their wives — well that too could wait. The present was golden.

The men chatted brilliantly, like a couple of politicians at a political rally: and when a good pun was delivered their roars of laughter could be heard for some distance.

Each time the treasured jar was put to the lips, the old moon looked down and laughed. So did John Barleycorn; and once the horse turned his head to look at the happy pair and to wonder why they had been so sparing with the whip.

The night was charming. A handsome night, to use a phrase coined by one of Tom's neighbors — a night for making love and a night for drinking grog. Who would ever have thought that on such a night disaster would be afoot?

Tom and Jerry were by this time well along in their cups and were planning on another such trip the following week, then all of a sudden there appeared beside them in the cart a ball of fire about the size of a dinner plate. It left the cart to pass between the beast's ears.

The now thoroughly aroused men jumped from the cart and headed for some bushes that grew beside the road. They stayed put until the ball of fire disappeared, then crawled back onto the highway.

But lo and behold the fire returned and burned up the horse and cart entirely. Then it formed a ring around Tom and Jerry, so that all avenues of escape was shut off. Was ever men in a worse predicament? Finally the circle of fire died out, leaving two very frightened people standing in the ashes.

Horrified the pair fled from the place as fast as their wobbly legs could carry them.

They naturally regretted the loss of the horse and cart, but the loss of the rum was their chief concern at the moment. With it they might find new courage, but without it, they knew for sure they were lost.

When they reached their homes early next morning everybody wanted to know what became of the horse and cart.

'That's a good question," piped Jerry. "You see, we was offered such a fancy price for the outfit by a rich man in the city that we decided to sell out and walk home."

Gold At Marshfield

When the news spread that a handful of gold coins had been found on the beach at Marshfield, great excitement ensued. Tall tales went speeding around the settlement — tales of enormous wealth lying buried, which could be gleaned for the price of adventure and a little digging.

Mr. W., a young fellow with a taste for adventure, and a group of local people hurried to Marshfield to try their luck at uncovering the treasure.

Locating the exact spot where the coins had been picked up, a tent was pitched and a fire kindled. Some of the group spent the entire night cutting firewood while the cook, John Lathers, prepared the evening meal of bacon, bread and beans.

The mosquitoes tortured them till their faces and hands swelled out of shape. They tore at their itching flesh, which almost drove them into a frenzy.

Next morning shovels and pick-axes were brought into play and the task of unearthing the supposed treasure got under way in real earnest. By evening quite a large excavation had been made, but as yet no treasure had come to light.

That night an Indian was seen slinking about their camp; and fearing he was trying to steal their meager rations, one of the party shot him. In the morning the body was buried where it lay; and all took a solemn oath never to say a word about the shooting incident to anyone.

After the burial the men went back to the pit and resumed work, as though nothing of importance had occurred.

Toward late afternoon of the second day, Mr. W.'s pick struck an object that was not rock or earth or metal. Great excitement spread through the little group of miners and they worked feverishly to clear away the loose earth.

Finally they uncovered the opening to a shaft, with a flight of wooden steps leading downward.

John Lathers, with pistol in hand, was the first to go down. He was immediately followed by Mr. W. and another gold seeker whose name the writer has not been able to learn. When the three reached the foot of the stairs all was as black as night, and they shouted to their companions above to throw down some candles.

When a light was struck they saw themselves standing before the entrance of a narrow passage that appeared to lead out under the river bed. The three advanced cautiously and in silence; something about the underground passage filled their hearts with an unknown fear.

There might be enemies lying in wait for them, or there might be spirits guarding the gold. Indeed, anything could happen in such a weird subterranean tunnel. The three drew close together as they continued to explore the passage.

They had covered about a hundred yards when the passage took a sharp turn toward the left and away from the river.

They were just making the turn when a great blast of air swept them full in the face, extinguishing the three candles simultaneously.

To add to their fears, a shot rang out, causing bits of loose earth to fall from the ceiling and walls. But the shot had come from Lathers' gun. He was holding the weapon at full cock when the gust of wind entered the cave and its force had thrown his hand against the wall, thus discharging the weapon.

Now that the other two knew the source of the shot, they were somewhat reassured; but what had caused the gust of violent wind? Where had it come from?

While this discussion was taking place, a low, moaning noise reached their ears. It was like somebody suffering great pain.

For the space of seconds the men stood and listened. The sound came a second time, much louder. The moaning was followed by some incoherent words that ended in hysterical laughter.

That was enough. Quickly the three retraced their steps, groping their way through the dark passage as best they could. Twice more the strange blasts of air swept down upon them, almost throwing them to the ground. Then, as they reached the foot of the stairway, the entire passage collapsed behind them with a defining roar.

The men who waited above saw three badly scared, wildeyed fellows climbing the stairs pell-mell.

"What's all the rush about?" they questioned. "You fellows look as if you'd seen a ghost."

"Didn't you hear that awful noise?" asked the others.

"Not us," said their spokesman. "Up here everything was as silent as sunset."

When the strange yarn had gone the rounds, every last one of them pulled stakes and left the place forever.

Tradition says that for many years the steps leading to the mysterious passage lay exposed to all who went to visit the spot. But the secret passage, where the moaning voice, mingled with the rushing wind, almost scared three gold seekers out of their wits, was never seen again by mortal eye.

What unexplained something was loose in that subterranean passage? To this day the mystery remains unsolved.

The Changed Babies

No doubt you have heard the yarn about the farmers who traded wives and lived happily ever afterward.

Well, I can't vouch for the truth of that story, but the one I am going to tell you now actually happened, and in the following manner:

In early days in this province, a landlord named Edward Smith, married a beautiful young lady by the name of Anetta Steward.

The couple were childless for six years before a baby boy came into their life.

Little Ronald was idolized by his parents, and they wished to have the child brought up with all the advantages that their wealth could offer. The first step was to employ the service of a competent governess, whom they located through friends back in England. Her name was Lillian Dale.

Mrs. Dale arrived in the Island in due time, armed with A-1 references and a baby of her own, about the same age as little Ronald.

Lillian Dale came from a good family, that could trace their family tree back four generations. No one could point the finger of scorn at Lillian or her ancestors. But came a day when the proud father drove Lillian from his home because she had married a good-for-nothing gambler who went by the name of John Henry Dale.

Dale met death by an accident three years later, but the proud father refused to have further to do with Lillian, even though she had a small son to take care of and no money to do it with. Lillian had married contrary to her father's wishes and he vowed that no part of his fortune would go to her now or after his death. Thus it came about that when Mrs. Dale was offered the job of governess she bundled up her belongings and her baby Phillip and sailed for Prince Edward Island.

One month later, she and Phillip arrived in Charlottetown and were driven immediately to the place that was to be her home until —

Lillian Dale was quick to observe the striking rememblance between Ronald and Phillip. Both boys were blond, blue-eyed and about the same size and age. Even from the first day the children were brought together, it was difficult to say which was which.

And as they grew, they remained as much alike as peas in a pod. Everyone who saw the children together took them for twins. Indeed, it often puzzled the mothers to tell them apart when naked.

But when Ronald was dressed in his expensive clothes it was another matter — the rich child vs. the poor child.

Mrs. Dale proved herself a competent person and the Smiths thanked their lucky stars that she had come to raise their boy. They felt sure that, under her care, little Ronald would have the sort of training he needed to grow into a real boy.

Edward Smith looked further ahead to the time his son would inherit his property and bring further honor and prestige to the Smith name.

Yes, the couple had implicit faith in the new governess, and she was left in full charge of the children while the Smiths were abroad.

Just when the tempter came to Lillian Dale we know not. What we do know, however, is that one day she switched the babies. Then she dressed her own son in Ronald's clothes. It was a daring and deceitful act, but she wanted her Phillip to have some of the good things of this world — money, fine clothes and etc. Would her evil plot ever come to light? Lillian thought it wouldn't.

When the Smith's arrived from Europe and picked up Lillian's child and hugged him as their own, she knew for certain that her act had not been discovered. Everything would be fine from now on she said to herself.

As the years passed and the children grew to young manhood, it became obvious to everyone that the landlord's son was a playboy of the first order. He was always getting into trouble and causing his parents deep grief. On the other hand, the governess' boy was a young man of dignity and worth.

The Smith's were puzzled as to why their only child should turn out so bad, while Lillian's son was so good. But things came to a head one day when the real Philip met death while swimming in a pool near his home. Lillian went on so that she finally broke down and confessed what she'd done.

Meanwhile Ronald was returned to his happy parents. At first the strange story was hushed up, but before Lillian Dale died she gave her story to the London Times, and now I am giving it to my readers in abbreviated form.

The Magic Stone

Centuries before the advent of the white man, the Algonquin Indians knew about the beautiful, nameless Island that rested like a gem on the bosom of the mighty St. Lawrence gulf.

What glowing tales about the island **par excellence** those red-skinned warriors must have narrated to their young and old folk, on the mainland and other far-flung places. What a pity, too, so many of those golden tales of a past era have been lost to posterity! When the French came to Canada, they found the Island still sparsely settled, still in the primeval state, a land of rare beauty and enchantment.

When they inquired the island's name they were told it was Minegoo and Binegoo it remained until the French changed its name to "Isle St. Jean."

Among the still remembered and perhaps most loved of the Indian legends, is the following, which I have translated almost word for word.

One day a French settler named Arcade Perry, while travelling a narrow, winding forest path, came to a tiny stream of water in which stood a red stone of peculiar shape and design.

The Frenchman tried in vain to wrest the stone from its setting, as he had hoped to remove it to his home for an ornament. Then he observed that he was being watched by a couple of Indians further up the stream. Perry beckoned them to come over to where he was. This they did, and then placed some green plants on the stone, after which they prayed to the great spirit.

Upon inquiring about this seemingly singular act, Perry was told the stone before them was a magic stone, held in awe by every Micmac on the Island, that many, many moons ago a mighty and proud Sauriquois Chieftain named Klatastan c a m e across the laughing Gulf Stream to visit some of his Micmac friends. The chief was accompanied by his daughter, Nistonia. For a while the pair lived in a large wigwam, near a stream supposed to be the abode of evil spirits.

All went well, until one day while father and daughter were walking along the bank, Nistonia accidentally trod on the foot of one of the spirits. This caused the Great Spirit to become angry and he sent Glooscap to tell the proud chief that his daughter would have to be sacrificed in order to appease the spirits.

"What! crief the Chief. "My daughter sacrificed to spirits. Never! Never! Never! Return to the great spirit, Glooscap, and tell him that Chief Kiotastan has spoken those words. Then bring back the great spirit's reply."

Early next day, Glooscap entered the Chief's wigwam and told him that instead of sacrificing his daughter to the spirits, he would order her changed into a beautiful magic stone, that would, if kissed, cure all manner of ailments.

After much pow-wowing with his subjects, the chief finally agreed to the idea, though not without much sorrow for the beautiful Indian girl was his only offspring, the joy and comfort of his middle age.

Legend says the transformation took place far out in the gulf stream while Chief Kiotastan was under the influence of some secret Indian drug.

When Nistonia, (Now the magic stone) was set in place, the chief was awakened from slumber and immediately transported on the back of a mighty eagle to the site. "Behold your daughter that was!" said Glooscap. "Now build your wigwam near this spot and our people never more will hunger or die of disease. "When you pass to the Happy Hunting Grounds the spirit of Nistonia will be there to give you a real Indian welcome."

A Case of Mistaken Identity

Ean MacDonald, together with his wife and three children arrived in the Belfast district aboard the Polly in 1803.

Like the other early settlers, MacDonald had to clear the land for a patch of potatoes, a bit of corn, and a crude shack.

In those days bears and wild cats were a pest and farmers were hard put to keep the former from running off with their infant livestock.

The first episode worth recording in the life of Ean MacDonald occurred one night when he was aroused from sleep by the squealing of pigs. Mac pulled on his trousers, picked up the old muzzle loader, and with one of his sons by his side, hit out for the pig pen.

Mama pig fought so valiantly to save her offspring that the thief took off empty handed. MacDonald and his son, Malcolm, followed in the pitch black night, determined that this time they would bag their bear.

A crashing among the forest limbs revealed where the thief had taken shelter. So father and son closed in for the kill. The theif made a break for freedom, caught his foot in some underbrush, and fell headlong into a bed of deep moss.

Instead of shooting the bear, MacDonald now decided to spare its life, at least for the present. A few clouts of a stout stick on its head would, he felt, render the animal unconscious long enough to get it to the barn.

Encouraged by his son's shouts of "Let him have it!" the father struck again and again at the now limp creature, until he was satisfied that handling it would present no danger to himself or his offspring. By this time the other members came on the run, and in their night clothing, to see what all the fun was about. Mrs. MacDonald had thoughtfully brought a l o n g a bull-rush torch, and when this was lighted and held over the prostrate form, Ean MacDonald wept like a child bereft of its parents, and no wonder, for instead of a bear he saw a dwarfed Indian — and he was dead.

The event caused a lot of wild, threatening talk from the redmen of the Island; and had it not been for the high estem in which MacDonald was held by whites and Indians alike things might have gone badly with him and his son.

Both were charged with the Indian's murder, but were later acquitted and given their freedom on the ground it was a mistaken identity.

The tragedy lingered long in the minds of the residents of Belfast; and caused so much grief to Ean MacDonald as to cause him to die prematurely.

The Warning Voice

The old pine and the little old woman beside it is a strange saga which takes the reader back to pioneer days.

Warren's grove, at North River, is where the old forest monarch lifted its majectic head to survey the whole countryside. Within this grove, and now completely hidden from the public view by thick underbrush, lies the ashes of the district's first dead.

The old pine tree served as a land mark for over a century, as it was much taller than its fellow trees, despite the loss of some 20 feet of its crown. Father time had withered its once proud form until its branches drooped like an aged man's drooping shoulders. In other words, the tree, at the time of our story, was but a skeleton of its former self.

Not far from the grove and the cemetery lived Margaret MacCormack, 10-year-old daughter of John and Mary MacCormack who were newly arrivals to the district from Northern Ireland.

Young Margaret, along with a couple of her chums, had gone to pick beechnuts in the grove, and to get to the exact spot they had to follow a narrow, winding path that led past the cemetery and the famous pine tree.

A slight wind was rattling the branches of the ancient tree as they went by but the children in their eagerness to reach the beech grove paid no attention to this.

In those days, beechnuts and hazel nuts could be found in great abundance all over the Island and custom demanded that the young fry gather them in season to be stored away until Christmas. It was a race with the squirrels to see which could carry away the most nuts in the shortest time.

Merrily the children chatted, and noisely the squirrels scolded the youngsters because they had dared venture on ground that they considered their sole right.

When the task had been completed and their little salt bags filled to capacity, the children headed for home, one walking behind another, sheep fashion, as the path was too narrow to accommodate more than one person at a time. Margaret was in the lead, some 10 or 15 feet ahead of the others.

They had passed the cemetery and were nearing the old pine, when a strange voice reached their ears. Looking in the direction from whence it came they observed a strange figure — an old woman, dressed in a garment of pure white. Her black hair hung in great loose masses over her shoulders and she was barefooted. They noticed too, that her arms were thrown about the pine as though she were supporting it.

The voice said over and over again:

"Don't come any nearer children." A moment more and they observed the figure release its arms from the tree. Then there was a mighty crash, and the old pine tree lay directly across the path the children were following, and not more than a few feet from where Margaret stood.

The Tattoed Arm

The scene of this true pioneer saga was Forest Hills. The character in the tale, Sandy Brown.

Brown, a batchelor, lived by himself, and made his living by cutting firewood for his elderly neighbors.

As a young man he had followed the sea, and like most sea faring folk he bore a tattoo. Not the tattoo of a beautiful girl, flags or what have you, but of all things the picture of a lone pine tree. Below the tree was Brown's name and place of birth, a sure means of identification.

Brown's hobby was hunting and killing bears. Those who visited his humble home on the outskirts of the forest, said its floors and walls were covered with a large number of cured bear hides, all brought to their present condition by the skilful arm of the forest recluse. The hobby kept Brown busy when he wasn't cutting down trees, and the skins helped to keep Jack Frost out of his shack, during the long cold winters, while their flesh provided him, at all times, with fresh and cured meat.

"You've killed and eaten a lot of bears," remarked one of Sandy's friends as they chatted together in Sandy's place one night. "But one of these days it will be the bear's turn to kill and eat you."

Both men laughed heartily at the joke, and Sandy said, "Well, sir, if ever I get inside a bear's belly I don't suppose anyone will miss me too much."

Not long after this meeting Sandy Brown was caught in a bad blizzard while prowling about looking for more bears to kill. Nobody missed him for over a week and then a search party got underway. They found his shack deserted and apparently hadn't been used for some time. Snow had drifted under the door sill and lay in a thin white streak across the floor.

All were satisfied that Brown had not been home for quite a while.

Doubts and fears now gave way to anxiety lest the fellow be found frozen to death, a common and terrible sight in pioneer days.

It was near sundown when the searchers came upon a fresh bear track. This they followed till they overtook the animal and killed it.

According to the custom of the times, they skinned the bear and removed its innards, so as to collect the valued fat from the carcass. This to be converted into soap by their wives.

The stomach of bruin was full of half digested flesh, proving that the animal had gorged itself recently. One of the men while fishing about with a stick, suddenly uttered an exclamation of horror.

One by one, they gathered round to see what Eric MacLean had discovered. What could that be inside bruin's stomach.? It didn't require a second look to convince the viewers that what they saw was part of a human arm — the tattooed arm of Sandy MacDonald.

Tradition Says Miser Was Eaten By Mice

At the age of 25, Isaac Barrett, or Shylock Barrett, as he was better known, had amassed a tidy fortune from buying and selling small fishing vessels. At 40, he was richer and meaner. His wife, a delicate woman is said to have died for lack of medical care and from lack of proper nutrition.

To save the expenses of a funeral, the old skinflint made the casket with his own hands and had one of his neighbors take her remains in a woodsleigh to its last resting place in one of Prince County's pioneer burial places — no marker was ever erected to her memory so that today nobody knows exactly where her ashes lie.

After his wife's death — the couple had no children — Miser Barrett went to live at Malpeque where he became a money lender, charging his clients exhorbitant rates of interest, and squeezing the very soul out of those that defaulted in their payments.

In those days a debtor could, and often was, thrown into prison for months on end, or until some good samaritan came forward and picked up the debtor's tab.

Barrett now lived alone in a weather-beaten shack which was without light or heat. He said he couldn't afford such luxuries and, anyway, nobody needed lights or heat in their homes. It was, he further stated, these very extravagances that keep so many people poor.

The years passed. The recluse miser grew richer with their passing — and meaner — so that in time there wasn't a single person in the community who didn't hate the very sight of his lean, ugly face. As one fellow put it, "That dam Shylock would do anything to put more shekels in his tin can bank."

Persons who borrowed from Skylock lived to regret it, for he always skinned them in the end, sometimes foreclosing on their properties when he knew they were hard up financially. Indeed, nothing mattered to Isaac Barrett except money, money, money! He counted his treasure by day and dreamt about it at night.

When he first came to Malpeque district he ate his meals at the home of Widow Claw, who needed the extra money, but later, he decided to prepare his own meals, saying it would cost him less.

So from that day until the time of his dreadful death, he subsisted on beans, cold water, stale bread, and mush, which never saw sugar or milk.

Come night, he would sit in his dreary cold shack, with nothing to keep the cold out save a few old rags and mats. Even under such miserable surroundings his thoughts were ever on his money, until it finally came to be his very god. Was there ever a foolisher man? Then came the plague of mice, or three plagues, to be more specific — 1724 — 1738. And these were no ordinary rodents — so we have been told. They were quite large as mice go, black in color, with short legs and flat claws.

In winter they lived in the forests and raised large litters. In spring they sallied forth to devour every vestige of crop they could come by. It has been said they ate the leaves from the trees as well. Between Three Rivers and Malpeque every green sprout went into their hungry bellies.

This destruction of crops caused the early settlers great tribulation and had it not been for the help the people received from Nova Scotia, many of them would certainly have starved.

During the last plague year, miser Barrett could not get in any of his interest money. And when he tried hard to press for it the whole countryside turned against him and might even have killed him had not the mice beat them to the punch.

Those that came begging a handout for their children were flatly refused, though the miser had stored up a good supply of food when he first learned of the rodent's advance.

When things were about at their worst, the great army of mice stormed the miser's place, broke into the cache of food and devoured it to the last crumb. In vain the old skinflint fought to save his precious supplies—and then himself, as the rodents fell upon him in great numbers, leaving behind them when they pushed on, a half eaten body — the body of Isaac Barrett.

No tears were shed over his bier, and some vowed he got exactly what was due him.

Historians tell us that two small vessels in Malpeque Bay suddenly found themselves surrounded by millions of those little savages. Soon the boats were crawling with rodents, and for every one the crews dispatched others climbed aboard to fill the gap.

But in the end they all drowned.

Legend of the Flying Bough Bed

Let me tell you the strange adventure that befell Fred and Mike O'Brien of Mitchell River, on January 15, 1835.

The brothers were on their way to Cardigan, via a forest path, when the great event happened. Both carried muzzle loaders, just in case they met up with some wild creature of the wood and were attacked.

While crossing a swampy region, Fred had the misfortune to walk into quick sand. He was rescued by his brother Mike after hours of toil and perspiration. However, this did not deter the two young fellows from pressing forward after they rested and had a sandwich.

Later that afternoon they sighted a small black bear and, in trying to follow the zigzag path, found themselves hopelessly lost by nightfall. And, to add to their dilema, a fresh storm swept across field and forests, filling the trail until the snow was knee deep.

There was nothing they could do under the circumstances but make camp for the night and hope for the best in the morning. But the card-matches they carried had become wet and so no fire could be started to thaw out their frost numbed limbs. This was, indeed, a predicament to be in and they recalled stories they'd heard about some early settlers having been found frozen to death under similar circumstances.

But being tired and hungry, by now, the brothers were soon fast asleep in their crude bough bed. When morning broke, they looked out upon a landscape of drifting whiteness, stirred into fury by a high wind. The cold too, was intense. It bit into their bones and made their teeth rattle.

While the boys were pondering as to what steps should be taken next, the moon appeared briefly from a cloud, and they were amazed to find themselves high in the air and not in the forest at all. However, they still were in the bough bed which kept sailing along through space like a rudderless ship.

After drifting aimlessly for some time, the pair dozed off to sleep, then awoke. The bough bed was still adrift in the sky, but horror of horrors, Fred was dead, frozen as stiff as a poker. Mike removed the dead man's clothing and put them on himself to help keep out the awful chill. Later, he tossed the body of his brother overboard and watched it descend to earth, till it was swallowed up in the storm.

The extra clothing felt good. So Mike began to weigh within his tortured brain the events of the past several hours. Had he actually tumbled the dead body of his brother from the bough bed. Was he actually riding the sky in a bed made of spruce boughs. And if so, why? Or was the whole thing just a dream, the sort of dream that comes to those about to enter the land of mist, on the other side of eternity. If a silly dream then all would be well when the dream ended.

A sudden jolt of the bough bed caused Mike to cast his eyes earthward, and what he saw gladdened his heart. Below him stretched the Cardigan River, ice bound now, but its course clearly defined, nevertheless.

Soon the mysterious ship — if one can call such a contrivance a ship, began to descend at a dizzy pace, causing Mike's stomach to go on the rampage. Then it landed with a bump that sent him head over heels onto the frozen shore.

Moments later, the first space man was on his way to Cardigan Village where he and his unfortunate brother had planned on going in the first place. Looking back toward the river O'Brien observed the flying-bough-bed taking off again and he just scratched his head.

The Legend of Sleepy Hollow

Sleepy Hollow is the name of a deep depression not far from Malpeque Bay. In early days it was used as a peaceful retreat by the Micmacs after the annual fall hunt. But after the advent of the white man to the Island, the Indians removed from Sleepy Hollow to the eastern part of the Island, and Sleepy Hollow became the abode of one of the strangest characters ever, and his equally strange dog, Fido.

The few whites who inhabited the district called the newcomer Fatty, though he was as lean as his dog. If he had another name nobody ever heard it for Fatty kept to himself and only spoke when he was asked to.

Those that knew the recluse best said he slept by day and gadded about by night, accompanied by Fido. Fatty would fill the air with his whistling and snatches of obscene songs, while Fido yelped and bayed at the moon, adding his weird noise to that of his master which led people to say that man and dog were crazy.

On moonlight nights the pair presented a queer picture as they roamed the countryside in search of what God alone knew — the lean, toothless dog and his aged master, whose long white beard trailed across his shoulders when the breeze caught it in its fingers.

Because Fatty was minus his left eye and had a peg leg some thought he was a pirate hiding away in Sleepy Hollow to escape the law. And the women and children shunned him as though he were Satan himself. Youngsters were not permitted outside their homes after sundown, and few men had the courage to enter the valley by night.

As time passed there grew up in the hearts of the inhabitants a hatred of the recluse and his dog, and they trumped up all kinds of stories about them, some so fantastic as to be almost unbelievable.

Then one winter when the snow lay deep on the ground and the north wind sent his chilly breath across the land, Fatty and Fido had not been seen for a couple of months and the settlers fell to wondering how they were passing the time. Some hoped they were dead, others thought the bad winter might have driven them from the valley and if so they might never return.

But when spring tripped across the Island with never a sight of the recluse or his dog, a dozen or so farmers decided to investigate. First, the searchers came upon the skeleton of the dog, the meat eaten clean from the carcass by foxes and birds of prey. Inside the miserable shack on a bed of bough lay the remains of the old man himself, his white whiskers embedded in a crust of ice and snow that had drifted into the shack through a number of openings.

The search party left the skelton of the dog lay where they'd found it, but they buried Fatty in a shallow grave and without benefit of clergy, under a lone pine tree. Then they burned down the shack before leaving the scene.

When the party had returned to their homes and told all that had taken place since their departure that morning, the women and children clapped their hands and shouted for joy. Never again would they live in dread of the hermit and his crazy dog, or so they fancied.

But not everyone rejoiced over the tragedy. There was one old man, for instance, who claimed Fatty had been accused unjustly by the people and that he wouldn't be at all surprised if his ghost returned to haunt those who had wronged him.

And believe it or not, that's exactly what did happen. Not only did the ghost of the recluse return to thwart and bedevil his enemies, but he brought his dog along as well, and the pair of them gadding about at all hours of the night put the fear of the Lord into everyone's hearts.

Mostly it was the sound of footsteps that were heard going up and down the stairs, followed by blood-curdling cries from man and beast. But sometimes Fido's voice could be heard in the forests mingling with the wild rollicking songs of its master.

Tradition says that the most haunted families left the hollow never to return. Some went gunning for the spirit of Fatty, seemingly forgetting that one can't kill a spirit no matter how hard one tries.

The whole place was in a dither when the Rev. Samuel Doe arrived on the scene. It seems the minister had the power to exercise spirits and he went right to work. In no time at all the reverend gentleman completed his task and thus it came about that Sleepy Hollow was rid of the ghosts of a man and his dog.

The Monster of O'Keef's Lake

A strange and rather startling yarn has to do with an unusual critter that inhabited O'Keef's Lake, and was last reported having been seen some eighty years ago. And right here, let me offer this bit of advice; if you are a timid soul forget about what you have read thus far and put the publication out of sight, for as you may have already guessed, it's a he man tale, one that is apt to make the hairs on your dome—if you have any left—stand on end. Anyway, it would seem to prove that old, old saying: "Truth is stranger than fiction."

The original script, written on a faded strip of brown wrapping paper, came into my possession while I was a resident of Kings County, Prince Edward Island, thirty years ago.

The manuscript came to grief when fire destroyed the dwelling where I'd placed it for safe keeping.

I persued the uncanny and almost unbelievable story so often that I am able, with out too many lapses of memory, to set it down here for your entertainment.

The odd yarn came to the ears of the first white settlers from Indians who believed the lake was the abode of an evil spirit, — a monster of large size and so fierce in combat that none could capture or destroy it. No creature living or dead was exactly like it, for it could appear and disappear at will as well as change form, which we are told happened from time to time.

The monster was held in such awe that even the bravest of the brave redskins, would not venture a canoe trip across O'Keef's Lake.

You have heard part one of the curious tale.

Part two takes us back to the year 1883, or to the summer of that year, to be more specific: "The sun was well along in the Western sky when two weary and footsore travellers sat down on the Lake's shore to rest, before continuing on their journey to Cardigan. In this manner began the greatest adventure of their lives, an adventure still narrated by old timers of the district whenever they get together to swap yarns about the good old days. But back to our tale.

One of the men took from his pocket a flask containing a very potent drink, which in those days was called spirits. (In a diluted form the same drink today would be labelled "Rum".) It was drained of its contents. Pipes were filled and lighted and the pair stretched out on the ground, the better to relax. Suddenly a terrifying roar rent the air, and the startled men, looked in the direction from which the noise came, and behold the oldest critter mortal eyes ever looked upon: "THE MONSTER".

This freak of nature was moving towards them, and when it drew nearer their eyes almost popped from their sockets, and little wonder, for the thing had a silver covered body fully twenty feet in length. The huge hump on its back supported a single fin some five feet tall and the color of yellow gold. However, the oddest thing about this odd creature was its head, large, and with but a single eye centered in the forehead. The eye is described as, being the shape and size of a saucer and having a certain fierceness about it like the eye of an owl; while dangling from the end of a long snout could be seen an appendage which closely resembled a tiny scythe.

Spellbound, the men watched the monster submerge, then rise to the surface and submerge again.

Their courage bolstered by the potent drink, they commandeered a rowboat and set out after the critter, heedless of whatever danger might be ahead.

Soon they reached the middle of the lake, where a second surprise awaited them. It was a sort of whirlpool, funnelshaped, and leading down through the water right into the lake's bottom. Why the mysterious water funnel had not been sighted and recorded before none could say, thought the manuscript speaks of a possible subterranean passage leading from the lake to the outside waters of the Gulf Stream.

While the pair pondered the strange events of the past half hour, the thing - or whatever one chooses to call it — rose to the surface and, bellowing loudly in apparent anger, charged the small craft with its daredevil occupants. There was not a moment to flee from the danger, or to fight the foe.

All was confusion; all sanity had apparently fled from the place and from the minds of the foolhardy adventurers. Now they found themselves under the water, struggling and fighting for breath; now they rose to the surface, cleaned the foam from ears and eyes and looked about in wonder. Everything was changed as if some magic wand had waved to create an entirely new scene. Gone was the mysterious water funnel. Gone too, was their boat. Only a few pieces of wreckage floated on the water to remind the men of past events. Luckily they were able to swim. Otherwise they too, might have disappeared along with the lake monster, never to be seen again.

The Wrong Pat

It was not an uncommon sight in pioneer days to see intoxicated persons at wakes and funerals. Indeed, there may be a few old timers still around who can recall the day the wrong Pat was almost buried in a tiny pioneer cemetery in King's County.

The first Pat, Pat Faley, lived alone in a small log cabin. His neighbors accused him of being over fond of the flowing bowl and often it was said, if he didn't stop his drink or at least slow down a little, he would surely fill a drunkard's grave — there were no alcoholics in those days — just drunkards.

To such warnings Pat Faley would say: I don't waste any money on women or clothes and besides, the liquor helps keep me well and active. Isn't that reason enough for me to keep right on drinking till I die?"

That same afternoon, (so the tale runs), Faley was seized with a fit and shortly afterward his bosom cronies found him dead on the floor of his rude shack. In one corner of the one-roomed cabin stood a keg of very potent rum. This the boys placed on the kitchen table, on orders from someone and forthwith they began to whoop it up.

Flynn was one of the party gathered there to celebrate the passing of their beloved neighbor. When it came to drinking the nectar of the gods, Flynn was Johnny on the spot, as the saying goes. Soon the entire group were as drunk as lords, and, what with toasts passing round, and snatches of old chanty songs the very rafters trembled. One never could find a merrier lot if one searched all over the Land of Minegoo.

The exact hour of Pat Foley's demise never was recorded, as none of the men present were sober enough to mark the time. Nor did they particularly care. Only John Barleycorn knew the living from the dead, and he didn't care either.

The morning of the second day saw the keg bone dry. A few of the souced began to stir in their drunken sleep. Outside in the nearby forest, a group of robins sang love songs to their mates, and a soft summer breeze swept through the open cabin door and fanned the fevered brows of the sleepers.

Before the afternoon was far spent, one drunk managed to stagger to his feet and tried to recall just what the celebration was all about. Somewhere in his subconscious mind he seemed to remember that somebody was dead; but he wasn't quite sure just who it was.

The next thing he remembered seeing was a coffin going out through the door.

What he didn't know was that the remains were those of Pat Flynn, while the deceased Pat lay on the floor, just as he had fallen in the fit.

Down the forest trail they went, the casket held high on their shoulders. When the body was about to be committed to mother earth there was no clergyman to be had within 100 miles of the settlement —a voice from within the shell cried out: "What's all this blatherskating about? Where am I? Get me out of this place before I smother entirely!"

Quickly shovels were tossed aside, and a group of frightened men were swallowed up by the forest. Before they could clear the woods, Pat Flynn was hard on their heels shouting and waving his arms and swearing that he'd bedamned if he was going to stand for bein' buried alive.

The Guiding Light

The following story came to the writer recently while visiting friends in South Melville, near Victoria Village.

The Guiding Light was seen by the late Duncan Matheson, of North River, when he went to see his sick brother, Robert, of South Melville.

The time of the visit, I was told, was late October, in the year 1899. Brother Duncan was driving a buggy at the time, and as he passed along the Green Road, he was taking in the beauty of the autumn leaves as they shimmered and danced in the night breeze. A full moon was riding high in the heavens, while in the distance could be heard the sharp yelping of a fox. High up in a tree the hoot of an owl came to Matheson's ears. Although he was not a superstitious man he had an uneasy feeling which he could not account for, a feeling that bad news was in the offing.

Matheson was about to light his pipe when the mare he was driving shied toward the side of the road nearly upsetting the old buggy. Quickly he tightened the loose reins to bring the beast under control. Then he laid the whip lightly on the animal's back and sides just to remind Nellie that no further nonsense on her part would be tolerated.

But Nellie shied again, this time nearly throwing the driver from his seat. Never before could Matheson recall such behavior and it made him a bit angry. Nellie would have to be taught a lesson in obedience and —

But the flash of a light in the area of the horse and buggy drove all thought of punishment out of the driver's head, at least for the t i m e being. Instead Matheson turned around to get a better look at the light or whatever it was. To his surprise the light came on again, this time in the shape of a baseball, though ten times as large. Fascinated, and, at the same time a wee bit nervous, Matheson watched the light drawn nearer and nearer. Now it disappeared beneath the vehicle and once more appeared right in front of them. The mare snorted, tossed her head from one side to the other, and lashed out wildly with her hind feet, until the driver feared she'd kick the buggy to pieces.

When, finally, he got things under control again, the light was moving slowly down the road and about 100 yards ahead of him.

The mare was still very nervous, but her master kept a tight rein, as on and on they journeyed till they came to the lane leading to the home of his brother. The light turned down the narrow country lane till it came to the farm house. Then it entered a bedroom window on the lower story and vanished from sight. Robert had followed its course with a stead eye and, as

1 said before, he was not one to panic or see things that were not there.

Right then he had a premonition that his brother was either gravely ill or perhaps dead. It took him some 20 minutes to unhitch Nellie, stable and feed her, before he entered the house. All was still as death itself inside. The family completely worn out from their long vigils with the ailing man were fast asleep.

Quietly Duncan entered the place, crossed the large hall and entered the bedroom occupied by his brother.

He was not at all surprised to see Robert's remains in a casket. The family informed him later that Robert had died the night before.

Was the guiding light a forerunner of death? Who can say? Certainly Duncan Matheson believed it was, and so did a lot of people who heard the strange and startling story.

Six-Inch Pedro

The Pedro family, who lived near the Pedro River, were married thirteen years before Mrs. Pedro gave birth to a six-inch baby, the smallest human ever born. Every day his parents expected to see him start growing like other children; but Six-Inch never added even a single inch to his stature by the end of twelve years. Although he was an active and intelligent boy his parents felt their pride wounded when the neighbors described their son as that little package of humanity who would never be worth his keep. Finally, in the boy's fifteenth year they decided to send him away.

Little Six-Inches did not complain. So one day he left home with nothing but the clothes on his back and a few pieces of gold.

After many d a y s travel he finally reached a small village ruled by a king, whose name was John Doe. Immediately he sought the king's residence and cried out in a shrill tiny voice: "I must see the king himself!"

His majesty, hearing the voice wondered and was greatly puzzled. First, he thought his ears were playing him tricks, but when the voice repeated the same sentence for the third time the king answered the door in person. His eyes opened wide when he saw the fellow standing there before him. "Come in," said the king, barely able to hold back a laugh. When they were seated, and Six-Inch Pedro was stuffed with good things to eat, the king listened to the lad's sad story, and immediately hired the little fellow as a page. The queen was delighted with her husband's decision to include Six-Inch among their servants. The lad became a great favorite, and before the month was over the Royal couple adopted him and gave him the name of Prince Six-Inch Pedro Doe. In this capacity he accompanied the king and queen everywhere they traveled, and though only a tiny creature he so appreciated his good fortune that he ever afterward conducted himself with honor and dignity.

One day while enroute to visit the Queen of Fairyland, the queen was attacked by a mad dog. The prince flew to her rescue and dispatched the savage beast by putting its eyes out with his tiny golden cane.

Needless to say her majesty was grateful for her deliverance, and told the boy the king was sure to reward him for his brave deed. On their way home the queen inquired of the boy what he would like in the way of a gift. "You have only to name it and the king will grant your wish," she told him.

"Well," said the prince, "in that case I should like to be as big as other boys my age."

When they returned to the castle and the queen had narrated the story of what had happened to her husband, the monarch was so delighted with the prince's courage that he gave him valuable presents as well as a private home of his own, staffed with servants.

But the greatest gift and surprise of all came the night that the king entered the prince's abode, followed by a magician who, after saying some strange magic words, changed Six-Inch into a large, well developed youth. Some years later the King died, the prince became king and married the royal couple's only daughter.

An Indian Legend of Miminegash

Miminegash is an Indian word. It was a sizable camping ground for Micmac warriors, long before the advent of the white man to the shores of Prince Edward Island.

According to our Indian legend, Manitu visited this camp site centuries ago and held a moon's talk with Chief Big Tide and his medicine man, Knockwood.

The meeting place of the big three took place in a stately group of trees, near the circle of wigwams. It was, of course, a private affair, save for the birds, the beasts, and the fishes that came to hear Manitu speak his words of wisdom. But Manitu's chief reason for the visit was to teach his people where the bear and the fox could be found in large numbers, where to fish for the best denizens of the sea; where to seek the wild duck and the geese, so that his people would never want for food; and last ly, to instruct the medicine man of the healing balm to be found in the vegetable and the forest kingdom.

And at night, when the red men lay fast in sleep and the flower children had folded their beautiful eyes, the stars of heaven glowed in the sky like a million diamonds, Manitu led the chief and the medicine man to a high hill from which he instructed them

Concerning the secrets of these heavenly bodies. Finally, when the pair had absorbed all the wisdom of Manitu's teaching, he left them for several moons, saying he'd return one day when they least expected him.

The day he came back to Miminegash was a great one for the Micmacs, and, after the event was duly celebrated, Manitu commended the medicine man and Father Big Tide to accompany him to the laughing waters of the Gulf Stream, where a canoe of gigantic size rode at anchor.

Silently the band of micmacs watched from a point of vantage, while their chief and Manitou boarded the canoe and were paddled far out into the water by a pair of winged spirits.

Farther and farther they paddled until all that remained of their vision was a tiny speck on the bosom of the deep. And while they strained their eyes lo a great fiery cloud came down from heaven and catching hold of the speck, carried it high up in the sky.

For many moons the Micmacs of Miminegash mourned the passing of their beloved chief. Meanwhile, the medicine man performed the duties of chief and doctor and, profiting from the instruction given him by the great spirit, counseled the people wisely and well. The seasons came and went. But one winter night when the fair bosom of Minegoo lay buried under a warm blanket of snow, and the Micmacs were gathered together in the warmth of their wigwams, a young brave who loved to star-gaze cried out to his fellows:

"See!" said he, pointing a finger heavenward, "there goes Father Big Tide and Manitou walking hand in hand along the great milky way. A path of light shadow showed their footprints on the Northern Lights.

Then all the people left their dwellings to gaze upon the wondrous sight, and while their eyes were turned upward and their lips were full of prayers, the great spirit addressed his people thusly:

"Mourn not, my children, for your mighty chief, Father Big Tide, nor for things that are past. Though we be separated for a season, I am always near to look upon you with compassion in your times of adversity. So fear not, not as long as the stars and the moon give light I shall provide for you and your little ones, always you shall be sheltered and fed and watched over until you, too, join your chief in the h a p p y hunting grounds.

"Soon will I send the springtime and the gentle south wind; soon will I cause the wild flowers to blossom and perfume the air with their fragrant breaths; and soon will I break winter's causeway and so that your canoes may once more venture forth upon the laughing Gulf waters and the inland rivers. Then will ye plant your crops and go forth to hunt the deer and the rabbit."

Having made his speech, Manitou waved his arm to his people and disappeared behind a cloud.

The Indians understood and were happy. Never again, they vowed, would they lie about their camp idle and grumbling over imaginary wrongs; never again would they complain or be unhappy, now that they'de seen with their eyes, Manitou and Chief Big Tide, high up in the heavens, watching and caring for them, as they wondered about in the lovely Island given to them by the Great Spirit.

Three Years Captive
Among the Micmacs

In the days when Malpeque was the chief Indian Village in this Island, they held captive for three years a white man by the name of Lawrence Poirier.

Poirier, a local fur trader and Smith, found it profitable to trade with the natives through their chief, Nataka Maquina, who was a dignified savage, six feet tall and well proportioned.

The dark copper-hued chief always went about with legs and arms covered with red paint; his eyebrows were shaded in black in two broad stripes, and his long black hair was done up in a high mound on the top of his head and plastered with bear's grease, the whole crown being powdered with white down, giving him a rather extraordinary appearance. Mantled across his broad shoulders was the skin of a sea otter, which reached almost to his knees and was fastened round his waist with a wide belt made from the bark of a tree. This fantastic hair-do and dress lent to the huge savage a look of magnificence.

Through years of barter Poirier and the chief became quite friendly, and while a visitor to the Indian village the Frenchman would set up a rude forge and make iron trinkets and steel arrows for the tribe.

One day Nataka came into the forge and, throwing down a gun whose lock had been broken, said:

"Look! Him no good."

The Frenchman, who was bad-tempered, called the chief a liar and threw the gun at his feet. Nataka frowned darkly but said nothing.

Two days later, when Poirier was about to depart, the chief ordered his warriors to seize him and make him a prisoner. In the ensuing scuffle a savage struck at him with an axe, making a deep gash in his forehead, so that he fell to the ground, dazed and bleeding.

When he came to himself, Lawrence Poirier was in the chief's wigwam. Water was brought and his face washed free of blood stains. Asked if he would be slave to the chief and make steel arrows for his bows, the Frenchman replied in the affirmative and was ordered to kiss his master's hand, which hs obligingly did. Meantime the people cried out for his death, but the chief turned a deaf ear to their pleadings. A tobacco leaf was placed over the wound in his head and he was permitted to lie down and sleep.

That night the savages danced a war dance around Nataka's wigwam and again asked for the death of Lawrence Poirier, the White Fox.

"I have promised the trader his life," said their leader, "and Chief Nataka Maquina never breaks a promise. Besides," said he," the white man knows how to make weapons we can use."

For three long years the paleface served the savage Nataka, doing whatever he was told. During those years he was obliged to eat muskrat, coon and other flesh food cooked and served a la mode.

Maquina one day informed Poirier that he must marry one of their women. Refusal would bring about his instant death.

Next day they boarded a canoe and paddle dacross Malpeque Bay to pick up a wife. We are told that he chose a young maiden named Upquesta. Then followed a great feast of herring spawn and frogs' legs.

Next, the chests were carried in, the gifts exhibited, the master of ceremonies explaining that all this treasure belonged to the white man and was offered by him in exchange for the girl. Nataka jumped to his feet and for over half an hour extolled the virtues of his slave. Then the bride's father sang the praises of his only daughter, saying he could never part with Upquesta, but ended his speech by agreeing to the marriage. The usual ceremony ended with a second feast and a rollicking war song whose echoes could be heard among the primeval forests.

The following morning Poirier got his wife from her father's wigwam and returned to their own side of the bay.

As the summer came and went, the white prisoner kept a sharp eye for passing countrymen and dreamed of plans for making his escape. But the months went by without any white settlers coming to the Indian village.

However, when spring unfolded her wings a party of French trappers were sighted making their camp not half a mile distant. A council was called at once to decide what should be done with the prisoner. Some wanted him scalped others thought it would be a good idea to hide him farther back in the forest.

Finally they asked Poirier himself what he thought about their plans and what he would like to do.

"I am happy here," he lied. "You have treated me kindly, and now that I'm married to an Indian I prefer to live with her always."

The chief drew himself to his full height and smiling down upon the Frenchman, spoke thusly:

"You send a letter to your friends, telling them you wish to remain with our people. Then they will go away satisfied."

Poirier agreed to this proposal, but the letter he wrote told of his being a prisoner in the hands of the Indians and requested that his release be effected as soon as possible.

Three days later, a large party of French settlers marched into the Indian village and demanded that their countryman be immediately handed over to their care.

This done, the chief expressed the hope that the incident might be forgotten, and in the future trade and good-will be revived between the two races.

Not caring to stir up trouble which might easily lead to a bloody massacre, the incident was closed and Lawrence Poirier was returned safe to his own home.

Fork in The Graveyard

Tradition tells us that fear killed **Peter MacIntyre**, a Scots immigrant who came to Tracadie, P.E.I. in 1772.

It was a bleak October night and a fine mist swept inland from the sea. Seated about the pot-bellied stove in the country store, a group of settlers discussed this and that subject till finally, they got around to current superstitions.

Then the door opened, and in walked big Peter MacIntyre. They made room for him in the seat, and Ben Peters kept talking about the light he claimed to have seen in the old French burying ground at Scotch Fort. It was (so Ben said), 'bout the size of a cart wheel and it lit up the whole cemetery so that the grave stones stood out in plain view."

"What nonsense, you talk," piped up MacIntyre, as he touched fire to his pipe. "I've been around here longer than most of ye and devil the thing I've seen that couldn't be explained. "Why fellers, I'd w a l k through the old graveyard this very night, and never give it a second thought."

"He talks brave when in the company of others," said Bill Jones. "Why we all knows the cemetery is haunted. Remember the —"

"Yer nothing but a bunch of superstitious women," said MacIntyre. "Ghosts and the likes of them are for the birds."

"Let's put him to the test," piped up old Ned Whalen. I'll bet a pound of tobaccy he won't visit the cemetery in a night like this and stick a hay fork in a grave to prove to us he's actually been there."

MacIntyre accepted the challenge and immediately set out for the graveyard fork in hand.

A visit to MacIntyre's shack next morning showed the place had not been occupied the night before, and four men set out to solve the mystery. When they reached the place of the dead, they were horrified to see the body of their neighbor slumped across a grave — and stone dead. A second look revealed a prong of the fork driven hard into the mound, and right through the tail of MacIntyre's long rain slicker.

Fairy Marriage at Cape Wolfe

Some two centuries ago a tiny birch bark canoe was sighted snaking its way across the Northumberland Strait headed for Cape Wolfe, where tradition says Gen. James Wolfe made a brief landing in 1759 on his way up the St. Lawrence on his conquest of Quebec.

The tiny craft, elevated at both ends like a new moon, was paddled by one named Gruko, a fairy prince of the great clan of MacLeebers.

Prince Gruko's mission to the crescent-shaped Island was to meet and wed Queen Watheria, the most beautiful of all Fairy Queens.

Not a breath of air ruffled the strait; a full moon and a host of twinkling stars smiled down on the lone voyager, as though they approved and welcomed the great event that would soon take place in the land of laughing waters and Little People.

The thought of meeting such a bewitchingly beautiful creature as Watheria had been pictured by those that had seen her, caused the prince's heart to beat faster and faster as he neared the cape. With cool, steady strokes he made the little craft leap forward at every dip of his paddle, leaving behind it a thin silvery wake of foam, like the silver lining against a dark cloud.

This was Prince Gruko's first visit to the Island of which he had heard so much about from his sires, and he was not disappointed when, finally, he moored the little canoe, stepped ashore, and viewed the magnificent forests stretching on every hand as far as the eye could see.

But beautiful as was the surrounding landscape, and melodious as was the songs of millions of feathered ministrels, all this was forgotten when he saw Queen Watheria standing alone on the shore and waving a huge eagle feather, the symbol of welcome, for she knew of Gruko's coming and had come down to the sea to greet him upon his arrival.

Perhaps my readers will feel curious to know what actually takes place when fairy royalty meets and especially when these two met, who had never set eyes upon each other before.

Luckily, I am able to give you a few of the details.

First, they rubbed noses after the Eskimo's fashion. Next they performed what is known as the fairy love dance, in which the dancers strut about like a couple of peacocks in their hour of glee. Finally they embraced, kissed each other, and then sat down on the sand holding hands, just like any couple would do when in love.

Now we see them standing close together; real children of nature, with little clothing to mar their perfectly constructed bodies.

Prince Gruko wore only a feathered loin cloth to which was sewn a little pouch to hold his bow and arrows. The queen wore a garland of leaves about her hips. The rest of her exquisitely proportioned form was partly concealed by a luxuriant growth of hair which reached right down to her dimpled ankles.

In other words, they were like the first human pair God created: Naked and unashamed and innocent of all wrong.

"You must be very tired," said the queen, "after such a long journey. And you must be brave too, to face the dangers of the deep all alone and in such a tiny canoe. Come, let us go to my palace for food and rest!"

The prince linked his arm in hers and together they set out for the palace which stood on the top of a smill hill overlooking the water.

For a time they continued on in silence, then the prince gave vent to his feeling by saying: "O, Queen, every movement of your graceful body fills me with a desire to own you; and when I look into your lovely eyes they remind me of dew drops in the heart of a lily."

Queen Watheria laughed a silvery little laugh and said:

"Can a Fairy Queen know when a male is in love with her heart or her possessions? Thus far our meeting has been ideal, let us not spoil it by too much flattery."

That ended the talk for the time being, and the pair climbed the golden steps leading to the palace and were escorted to its interior by two of the smallest creatures Gruko had ever seen. Later he learned they were the queen's favorite maids who attended to her majesty's needs day and night.

The floors were made of inlaid colored marble, while the walls and cailings were decorated with hand carved figures of fairy gods and angels. Half a dozen winding stairs led to upper rooms, where the scent of myriads of flowers filled their nostrils with delight. Here, too, flowed a fountain of a pure white substance that resembled milk, but was much swetter to the taste. The palace was lighted by a magic wand and the lights were extinguished by the same method. Indeed, the magnificence of this fairy castle would be hard to picture by any pen. All I can say is that our palaces are crude along side of this one.

Having passed through the various rooms and observed its many wonders, Prince Gruko and the Queen were escorted to the banquet hall where they dined on such delicacies as mushroom on toasted dandelions and drunk a wine of such superior quality that Gruko pronounced it "The nectar of the gods".

It would require the pen of a genius to describe in detail half the wonders to be met with within the walls of this ancient edifice; so we must hurry along to the scene of the wedding — the wedding of Prince Gruko and Queen Watheria — which took place the next day, with thousands of invited guests in attendance.

The ceremony was simplicity itself. The regal couple stood beside the throne, with silvery winged angels on each side, while one in the robe of a priest bade them drink a kind of honey nectar from a gold cup. Having carried out this order, the couple embraced each other and the cereomny was ended.

During the remainder of the day, there was singing and dancing and laughter, in which Prince Gruko and his happy bride took part. Tradition says the wonderful couple lived happily in the wonderful palace for many, many years, or until the Little People moved elsewhere.

Position of the Legendary

Pool Still Controversal

Some local historians place the pool of Mineotta near Malpeque Bay, but my Indian friends from whom I get this legend, say the famous pool was in Kellow's Hollow, near the present village of Cornwall.

Chief Sunlight had two children, a boy and a girl. The boy was named Petre, the girl Mineotta, the most beautiful and clever maiden in all the fair island of Minegoo. And it was Mineotta for whom the pool was named.

Let me tell you the tragic story:

When not occupied with the affairs of state, Chief Sunlight would call his wife and together they would wander to the pool, where for hours they would sit and talk about the strange water spirit that dwelt therein.

They had not long been seated when they were joined by Petre and Mineotta, and the chief took advantage of the occasion to warn his adventuresome son never to cross or even to swim in the sacred pool. To do so would cause the spirit to become angry. Indeed the thing might even demand a human sacrifice if unduly disturbed.

"What nonsense you speak," said Petre. "I do not believe the tale. The story was born in the head of some imaginative person who might better have spent his time hunting the fox. Have I not slain the fleet-footed deer and brought to earth the sharp-eyes eagle? Why should I not destroy the pool spirit if such a creature does exist and then our people would be done with the silly story?"

"Silence!" said his sire. "You, my son, are full of youthful ignorance. No one can kill a spirit. A spirit has neither flesh nor blood like the fox and the deer. How often must I tell you the old prophecy among my people, namely, that the warrior foolish enough to speak ill of the spirit or swim in the scared pool will himself be destroyed and sucked down into the subterranean passage that leads from the bottom of the pool to the Gulf Stream. Besides, the act would endandger the lives of all the people. Let me hear no more of this silly talk."

Then the chief and his wife left the pool and started for the Micmac village, some 200 yards upstream.

Howver, Mineotta and her brother lingered on and for some time discussed together the strange story.

"It's just another myth," said Petre. "I've a good mind to swim across the water right now, spirit or no spirit."

"Oh! No, no," protested his sister. "You

heard what our sire said. Such a rash act might endanger us all! You must not do it!"

"Well," replied Petre, "If a spirit can't be killed I can see no harm in crossing the pool now or at any future time. If I cross the pool and the spirit comes at me I'll kill it with my trusted bow and arrow. This will make me the greatest warrior in Minegoo and all the people will shout with joy—"

"Silence!" cried Mineotta. "Your boastful words have already caused the water of the pool to become angry, and can't you hear the mournful voices of the Spirit lamenting your wild words? You, my brother, should bow your head in shame."

They talked on and on, until the angry water grew quiet and the voice of the spirit was lost among the echoes of the forest. Then Petre picked up his bow and arrow and disappeared into the forest.

When he returned to the pool late that same evening his beautiful sister had gone and he called her name loudly, but only the echo of his own voice could be heard in the distance. Then he spied Mineotta and his father, standing on the opposite bank of the pool and heedles of the latter's warning he started swimming toward them, thus cutting the distance between them and himself by a full half mile.

His sire recognized him when about half way across and shouted for him to turn back, but it was advice offered in vain. A funnel-shaped wave caught Petre in its mouth and dragged him down, down, down, till he was lost from view. Then Chief Sunlight lifted his eyes toward the sky and moaned sadly: "He was my only son. I must avenge his death come what may."

"Stop it!" said Mineotta. "Put aside your weapons, sire, for did you not say yourself that no one could kill a spirit? Come, let us leave this terrible place forever before you commit the unpardonable sin."

The chief made no reply. He stood like one in a trance, with eyes fixed on the spot where his offspring had disappeared.

They both saw it as the same time, a strange fish-like creature that rose to the surface, looked accusingly at them with its one eye. When it began to submerge the chief drew his bow and sent an a r r o w straight into its heart. A brief struggle followed and then the pool spirit went down in a lather of foam to join Petre at the bottom of the pond.

The sun dropped beneath the western horizon and all was stil as death itself. Even the birds ceased their melodious songs. Were they waiting for a epilogue to the recent tragedy?

The tide came in where there was never a tide before. It would have swept the chief off his feet had not his daughter pulled him to safety. After this they heard a hissing sound like steam escaping from a faucet.

Again, Mineotta pleaded with her father to leave the spot at once, but he said, "No, daughter, I must see the end of the drama. I have committed the unpardonable sin and neither my people nor the Great Spirit will pardon me."

From the sky a long arm reached down and touched the head of the beautiful princess. Legend says it was the arm of Glooscap. Anyway, Mineotta was quickly changed into a spirit creature clothed in misty clouds. As she stepped into the sacred pool she cried loudly:

"I am the sacrifice foretold by the prophets. Henceforth the pool shall bear my name."

Many Island Indians still believe the legend, though the pool has long since ceased to exist. They believe also that the spirit of the beautiful princess still wanders through Kellow's Hollow.

Legend Has It That A Ghost Operated Scott's Grist Mill

Only a stone's throw from the home of the lady who writes "Ellen's Diary" stands an old grist mill. Today it is known as Chowan's Mills; but in early days it was Scott's Mills, owned and operated by the late John Scott and his sons.

When the mill first was opened to the public it was well patronized by farmers, because the miller had a reputation of turning out the best flour made in Queen County.

Legend says that strange things happened around the old mill during early days. Take for instance, that night when members of the Scott household were too ill to attend to the grinding of a great pile of wheat which lay in sacks all about the mill.

John Scott was sitting beside a cozy fire in the kitchen of his comfortable home. In an adjoining room lay his two first-born children; upstairs his wife raved aloud in a fevered condition. He, himself, was ill. Indeed the whole family was sorely stricken with an illness that had the doctors baffled.

Scott, being a good miller and the type of man that worried about such things as unground wheat, suddenly heard the mill groan, and began grinding.

Believing that somebody was meddling with the machinery, Scott put on his coat and hat and started down the steep hill which separated mill and home.

When he drew near the building he noticed a lighted lantern hanging on a hook outside the main entrance. He couldn't remember having left the lantern lighted. But then, of course, whoever was snooping about the place must have put a match to it.

Now a bit angered at such a sight, and because he had been obliged to turn out in his present condition, he quickened his pace and clutched more tightly the stout stick which he had just picked from the ground.

The noisy throbbing of the machinery grew louder, and from the half-opened door of the mill he could see a thin vapor of dust floating out over the air, its presence made visible by the rays of light.

Quickly Scott stepped across the flume, flung wide the door then stepped inside.

The mill was in apple-pie order—and running. The hopper had been filled with grain, and bags were fitted snugly to the mouths of the elevators, awaiting the flow of flour.

In the centre of the mill a second light dispelled the surrounding gloom; and, while the miller made a mental note of this, the sound of footsteps coming down the stairs could be heard distinctly.

Seconds passed.

Then the object of Scott's search came into view, descended to the floor level, crossed to where the hopper rested, ran fingers through the grains of wheat after the manner of an experienced miller.

Scott was about to address the intruder when the outside door of the mill closed with a terrific bank. When he turned to ascertain the cause of this noise, both the lights were snuffed out as if some magic breath had blown upon them.

Then the wheels of the mill began to slow down, their creaking axles creaked less and finally all was silent.

Miller Scott was not the sort of person who scares easily. So, searching through his pockets, he found a match and touched its fire to the extinguished lantern within.

All was silent as death. Not an inch of that building did he fail to search thoroughly. Yet there was nobody to be seen.

The identity of the strange miller remains unknown.

But the legends persists that three bags of flour had been ground and not by Miller Scott.

The House of Death

It stood on a rising knoll of land overlooking the Northumberland Strait, near the place now called Wolfe's Cove or Cape Wolfe, if you prefer. For it was at this very spot that the great English General landed briefly in October 1759, on his way to the conquest of Quebec.

And it was a strange sort of building, to say the least. Built by an eccentric, wealthy Frenchman who wished to be as far away from civilization as possible, the "house of death", as it later became known to the travelling public, was, in truth, a combination of styles and so large that it commanded the attention of all who saw it. The outside was partly made of red native sandstone and partly of split pine boards gleaned from the surrounding forest, while the interior was done in paneled spruce and birch, overlaid with fine grained walnut and mahogany. The wide stairway leading to the second and third stories could accommodate four persons walking side by side. The place boasted thirty large rooms and as many cubbyholes and secret passage ways. All in all one might call it a fantastic waste. This architectural monstrosity was the home of Mr. and Mrs. Perry Martill and their six offspring.

They say the Martills immigrated to the Island from France early in the 17th centtury, though there are no records to substantiate the story. To build this strange habitation Martill employed only his own countrymen and, when the task was completed, he packed them all off to their own country.

How Martill came by his wealth none could say. Nor could anyone hazard a guess as to his past life, or why he had chosen such a god forsaken spot as the cove for his home.

After a residence of only one year the family were reduced by sudden and violent deaths to one person — Perry Martill. Four of their six children were drowned; two got lost in one of the houses narrow passageways and had been suffocated to death before their bodies were discovered. This awful tragedy so upset the mind of Madam Martill that she hanged herself from a beam in the kitchen ceiling.

From that day on the place was named the "House of Death", and few persons cared to be seen about the place let alone to cross its threshold.

Soon a f t e r these tragic occurrences Martill himself became fed up with living at the cove. The loneliness and past memories prompted him to leave without saying a word to anyone. He was never heard of again. Not a single piece of furniture had been removed. Indeed everything was exactly as it had been when the family were all together. The place remained unclaimed and unoccupied for the next couple of years. Then an Englishman and his aged sister came to dwell therein. But their stay was short. The sister died suddenly in her sleep, and the brother moved out bag and baggage, never again to return to the House of death.

The years passed, until one night a great gale swept across the straits, destroying many fishing vessels and the homes of their owners. The storm descended on the huge mansion with the fury of a fiend, as though it would wipe out every trace of the recent tragedy. The roof was carried away together with a section of the west wing, leaving the structure prey to rain, snow and time. Under such conditions, it was not long before the fine furniture lay in a heap of ruins. Then part of the stairways, as well as the floor, fell into the cellar. So nothing but a crumbling mass of ruins could be seen that morning when General James Wolfe came ashore at the cove and, while his men were putting aboard a fresh supply of water from a nearby spring, the general himself took a short walk along a narrow trail that led directly to the crumbling ruins.

Surprised to see such a mass of ruins in such an out of the way place, Wolfe's curiosity was aroused to such an extent that he crossed the rotting threshold and looked around — Everywhere was death and decay. He had never heard of the place nor had any of his men and the mystery deepened. From that time on a melancholy fell over Wolfe, a melancholy that was observed by every member of the crew and no words of theirs could bring joy to his sagging spirits.

Coming face to face with the old battered and forsaken house, seemed to have had a bad effect on the general. Perhaps its former glory and then utter ruin, impressed upon Wolfe's mind the butchery of war and the vain glory of conquest.

Anyway, as the little flotilla moved down the broad St. Lawrence in the current of the ebb tide, Wolfe quoted this prophetic line from "Gray's Elegy In A Country Churchyard:"

"The paths of glory lead but to the grave."

Daughters of the Stars

Once upon a time, there lived near Malpeque Bay a group of Indian maidens so beautiful that the angels of heaven came to earth to feast upon their loveliness.

This group (so the legend runs) were born daughters of the stars, and they possessed wings which enabled them to fly away to any habitation they chose to visit.

These angelic like creatures were discovered by a party of hunters, in a deep valley, hidden from the eyes of all passers by a dense mist that perpetually hung over the enchante darea.

It was the sound of melodious music that first lured the Indian hunters to this secret abode; heavenly music, and the blending of sweet-voiced maidens who sang their songs in the Micmac tongue.

Bewitched by the enchanting singers, the hunters pushed through the dense mist and soon entered a valley, whose Edenlike loveliness haunted them for the rest of their lives.

Beside a milk white lake, sat the daughters of the stars, robbed in snow white feathers and holding in their red-colored hands giant palm leaf fans. These they waved gently in front of their faces as the day was sunny and quite hot.

Upon seeing the hunters, the maidens sprang to their feet and, moving gracefully step to step, advanced to welcome the strangers. As they drew nearer the men noticed for the first time that each maiden possessed a set of silvery wings, folded close to their bodies. Fortunately, all spoke the same language, and soon they engaged in conversation which led to many pleasant talks. The winged creatures now conducted the hunters down a flight of steps which led into a vast canyon lighted by innumerable stars and a moon in its last quarter. In the center of the canyon was a huge lake on whose bosom the hunters were quick to observe many, many tiny canoes, paddled by persons so small they looked for all the world like midgets.

"Now," said the maiden who was a bit more beautiful than the others, "Look towards the east and tell me what you see."

Turning in the direction indicated, the hunters were astonished to see a large orchard whose trees were laden with a great variety of fruits, all wind-blown and ripe enough to be plucked. Though the men knew not one fruit from another they ate several varieties, all of which they pronounced delicious.

To the west, flowed a river red as blood and, when the hunters inquired about this phenomenon, the maidens replied in unison: "The river you see before you is the river of Light. This is where the great Spirit

Himself comes to bathe and rest from His great travels among His people. Once upon a time its water was white but many warriors met death at this spot in ancient feuds and ever since it has flowed deep and red as you now see it."

The sight of so many wonderful things so occupied the minds of the intruders that they completely forgot their mission and went off in search of other wonders.

Upon returning, the daughters of the stars, invited their unbidden guests to a feast such as no Micmac hunter had ever seen before: stuffed turtle doves, mushrooms topped with a jelly like cream, powdered maize, and oysters so large and luscious that the great Spirit himself would have keenly relished. The food was followed by a sweet-tasting nectar which, they were informed, came from the fruit of a certain tree in the orchard. While the hunters were slowly sipping the mysterious and delicious nectar, the maidens narrated the following story of their origin and why they possessed wings:

"As you know, it is considered disgraceful to have food if your neighbour has none. To be a creditable member of the Red race one must divide one's possessions with those that are less fortunate.

"This law of the Indian was broken by a party of greedy warriors. A full scale war followed in which hosts of our people were arrowed to death. But being born of the stars we were called to a council meeting presided over by Manitou the Mighty and presented with wings so that we might fly away to this happy habitation which you have entered illegally—"

The rest of the story must remain untold, for by now the strange drink had taken such an effect on the listeners as to cause them to fall into a profound sleep.

How long they remained in the arms of Morpheus will never be known. And when, at last, they shook off the stupor and opened their eyes, they looked about for a sight of the maidens but they had vanished, as though they'd never been. Gone, too, was the enchanted valley and all its wonders. Even the great River had dried up, leaving naught but a dry twisting path through which it had once flowed in all its majesty.

The men returned at once to their wigwam homes and told their people the strange and startling story I have set down for your entertainment.

Some believed the saga, while others scoffed at the tale, and accused the hunters for not returning with food for the little ones.

Time and again they sought the secret valley and its beautiful inhabitants, but all in vain.

In talking with old Indians, I find this legend to be the most widely known and thoroughly believed, in the whole saga of Indian folklore.

Devil Stole The Rum

Prince Edward Islanders boast of their marvelous summer climate, the Hill of Fairies, the phantom ship that sail the Northumberland Strait at least once every decade, and Kellow's Hollow, scene of many a hairraising saga in pioneer days; but few know about the Devil's Punch Bowl of how it got its name.

The Devil's Punch Bowl may be seen near Hazel Grove. According to legend, it has existed since early pioneer days, when the old Boy himself stole a 90-gallon puncheon of rum from John Hawkins who was hauling the precious nectar from the capital to the local tavern keeper at Hazel Grove.

In those days, the roads leading out of Charlottetown were little better than cow paths, and they were rough as well. So in order to keep the oxen-driver, stone boat and its precious cargo from over-turning, Hawkins had secured all with a stout rope.

The first leg of the tiresome journey proved uneventful and Hawkins whistled a few lively tunes, while he gently goaded his oxen to increase their slow pace. When, finally, the last hill had been ascended and the journey about completed, the driver drew up to give the faithful animals a brief rest.

Suddenly, the air was rent with a burst of hilarious laughter, followed by the appearance of his Satanic Majesty, replete to horns, hooves and tail, the latter curled in rings around Satan's nude body.

In his right hand was firmly gripped a three-tined fork while a huge silver cutlass dangled from a leather belt on the right hand side.

Brave man that he usually was, John Hawkins cowered at the sight of such a formidable foe, and to the old boy's hearty, "Good day Mate!" poor Hawkins uttered not a word.

Without wasting further words, the Devil came forward at a quick pace and, drawing the cutlass from its place, he handed the wicked looking blade to our hero and ordered him to cut the ropes pronto.

When the huge puncheon was free of its fetters, the old boy gave it such a powerful shove that it went crashing down the hillside taking everything in its path.

How the Devil managed to ride the thunder bolt Hawkins couldn't even hazard a guess; but ride it he did, till it had run its course and sank beneath the surface, leaving a round gaping hole—the Punch Bowl. While Hawkins looked on in amazement the Devil let out a blood-curdling laugh and disappeared into the depression.

Then, if matters were not already bad enough, the oxen broke from their harness and fled into the forest, leaving poor Hawkins stranded and half frightened to death.

The following day he arrived back in Charlottetown and told his fantastic story. Some believed the saga, but there were others who openly accused him of stealing the stuff and selling it for personal gain. These charges Hawkins stoutly denied, and swore he could prove every word he'd spoken.

"Looks like hoof prints," observed one of the doubters, who accompanied Hawkins to the scene of the recent miracle. "But they are different somehow." A little further on, Slim Peters picked up part of an ox yoke and one side of the crude sled, all of which did much to substantiate Hawkin's yarn; but he was not entirely in the clear.

The small group of men who had come to investigate wanted to see the hole into which their leader had alleged the Devil and the puncheon had disappeared.

A short walk brought them to the spot. "There she be," said Hawkins, pointing a trembling finger at the newly made depression. And while the group gazed at the bowl in awe, its bosom rose and fell in quick beats, like a person with a hard athmatic attack. They were quick, too, to note a strong odor of liquor, mixed with burning sulphur. Had the party needed m o r e convincing (which they didn't), they got it, when from the depth of the pit came the sound of laughter and the clinking together of glasses. This was quickly followed by a voice which Hawkins had no trouble in recognizing:

"Drink up, me hearties, and be merry, for the drinks are on John Hawkins, who is now standing outside the pit together with some of his cronies."

"Enough is enough," John Doe said, "Let us get away from here while the going's good."

"It's the Devil's Punch Bowl sure enough," said another, "or I'll eat my hat," and that, incidentally, is how the place got its name.

Ship's Mate Changed

Into Mermaid

Captain Fred Winkle was discussing strange sea creatures with another deep sea captain aboard his sailing ship the "Black Ace" as she rode at anchor in the harbor at Charlottetown, Prince Edward Island. The date was June 6th, 1803.

Finally mermaids came under discussion; those curious creatures with the upper part of the body like that of a human and the lower part all fish.

"Well, sir," said Captain Dithers, "them things may exist, but so far I've never seen any."

"You haven't?" observed Capt. Winkle, "Well, I have. Off the coast of China and once near the entrance to Charlottetown Harbor. What beautiful creatures they are!"

"Yes, and these daughters of the sea can sing like canaries. Sailors have been known to desert ship due to their charm."

"You say you saw 'em at the entrance to this harbor. Pray when was that?"

"In the spring of 1801, continued Capt. Winkle, "I left Charlottetown to pick up a cargo of freight in Sydney, Australia. We were some 20 miles from port when I left my cabin for a stroll on deck, the day being a handsome one.

"My 1st officer was leaning over the ship's rail, gazing intently at the water below. Upon closer observation I was astonished to see a couple of mermaids swimming rapidly toward the Black Ace. A moment more and they drew up alongside my ship and began to work their magic spell on the mate, who appeared to be in a state of trance. He had never seen any of the little cuties before and they intrigued him.

"I left the mate with a parting warning not to lose his head over the sea gals; but when I came on deck later I was amazed to see a pile of discarded clothing where the mate had stood.

"Lifting my binoculars to my eyes I was able to see three objects swimming some distance from my ship."

"What happened after that?" asked Capt. Dithers. "Never heard such a sea tale in my life."

"We had to proceed without my first officer. Naturally, I was sorry to leave such a fine fellow to the mercy of the sea gals and I reckoned that once they'd tired of his company they'd sent him packing to Davie Jones locker..."

At this point the narrator stopped to wipe

his brow, the day being quite a warm one. Then he continued:

"I picked up a new mate in Australia before making the return voyage. The trip proved uneventful — that is, until the Black Ace re-entered the area where this saga began. Suddenly three sea daughters appeared not more than 50 yards from the Black Ace. There was no mistaking my first officer. I recognized him instantly from the sabre cut on his left cheek, the result of a fight he'd had some years before in Hong Kong.

The head itself was about the size of a half grown turnip. Somehow the sea gals had managed to change my mate into a mermaid.

Jean La Belle And Pedro

In the little village now called Victoria, in the Garden of the Gulf, there lived many years ago, while the Island was owned by France, an unique character of the name of Jean La Belle.

Where he hailed from, or why he chose to make his home in the wilderness with only a parrot and wild beasts to keep him company, no one could say.

The settlers nicknamed him Robinson Crusoe on account of the skins of animals he wore instead of proper clothing. And the abode he lived in was equally strange; constructed wholly of poles, brush and birch bark.

Seldom did Jean LaBelle leave his forest retreat, preferring to spend his days with his pet, Pedro, a bird of ill repute that chattered and cursed, cursed and chattered, from atop its masters shoulder, from morning till night.

The few Indians who made brief stops at the fantastic place feared the parrot as though it was the very devil. They even claimed the bird put a spell upon them, so that they lost direction while travelling through the forest. As for La Belle himself, they considered him shifty and sly like the fox; mostly they gave the place a wide berth, as the saying goes.

La Belle was a fellow of few words. And when anyone asked him a direct question he made no reply, which was just as well as nobody would believe what he said anyway.

On a warm sunny day in the year 1760, a local fisherman by the name of Parry Martell, while setting his fishing gear in waters off the Gulf Stream, observed La Belle and Pedro entering a cavern some eighth of a mile from where his small boat rode at anchor. For over an hour he waited for their reappearance and when they did not leave the cave he returned to his home.

This cave, while well known to the settlers, had never been explored by any of them. The Indians said the place was haunted; full of evil spirits; that anyone entering the place would never come out alive.

Ten days after this event, Indians reported to the settlers that La Belle and his parrot had disappeared. Gone too, was his crude dwelling. Someone had reduced it to ashes.

Recalling that he'd seen the pair entering the cave some days ago, Martell called a few of his neighbors and asked whether or not they would join him in searching the cave. Only three volunteered. The others would have nothing to do with the venture, stating that they feared the place and, besides, they didn't give a damn whether La Belle was ever found.

194

With a handful of candles, the three set out determined to solve the mystery, come what may.

Once inside the cavern candles were lighted and the men pressed forward in single file. Soon they came to a spring of water bubbling joyously from the heart of a large rock — all was still as death save for their own whispered words. A few yards farther they ran into a flock of bats, confused and angry on being awakened from slumber. The trio got quite a scare until they realized it was nothing worse than a lot of angry bats.

The exploration continued; and twice Martell called out at the top of his voice:

"Oh Robinson Crusoe!"

There was no answer. On and on they went till finally they reached the end of the cave. Except for the bats and themselves, the place was as bare as Mother Hubbard's cupboard.

The $64 question: What had happened to La Belle and Pedro? Well, all kinds of stories began to circulate. The Indians believed they were eaten by the evil spirits; the more superstitious among the French thought that the pair might be hidden in some secret nook in the cave by ghosts. However, Martell came up with a plausible answer. Namely: that La Belle was a pirate, that he had taken to the forest to escape the long arm of the law, that a pirate ship had entered the strait one dark foggy night and that La Belle and Pedro boarded the ship and sailed away to parts unknown.

—